HIGHER MATHS

HIGHER GRADE COURSE NOTES

KEN NISBET

ISBN 1-898890-26-9

Published by
Leckie & Leckie
8 Whitehill Terrace
St Andrews
Scotland UK KY16 8RN
tel: 01334 475656
fax: 01334 477392
email: s.leckie@leckie-and-leckie.co.uk
web: www.leckie-and-leckie.co.uk

A CIP Catalogue record for this publication is available from the British Library.

Special thanks to
Julie Barclay (design), Wendy Nightingale (page make-up), Alex Robertson (editing), Bruce Ryan (project management), Hamish Sanderson (illustration), Norman Stewart (production assistance) and Eliana Wilson (typing)

This book has been printed on paper which is made from 100% genuine waste. No chlorine bleaching has been used in the manufacturing process.

The cover has been printed on art board which is made from 25% de-inked post-consumer waste, 25% pre-consumer waste and 50% chlorine-free fibre and is the most environmentally sound art grade board available.

This paper and board have been used for the benefit of the environment.

Printed in Scotland by Inglis Allen

Leckie & Leckie

Introduction

These *Course Notes* are intended to prepare you for the SQA Higher Mathematics Exam. They have been written to fit the Unit structure of the Mathematics Higher course as laid down in The National Course Specification document.

This structure is:	Mandatory	Mathematics 1 (H)	(Unit 1 of these Notes)
		Mathematics 2 (H)	(Unit 2 of these Notes)
	Optional	Mathematics 3 (H)	(Unit 3 of these Notes)

The optional Statistics (H) unit is not covered in these Notes. The 'Higher Still' course will first be assessed during the session 99/00. However, as the content of the Higher course has not undergone a change, these Notes also provide an ideal set of revision notes for the Higher Maths Exam during session 98/99 (the traditional 'Revised' Higher Exam).

Key points have been emphasised, facts have been clearly summarised and all vital techniques illustrated with a host of worked examples. The language used and the style of explanation are such that you can easily relate to the ideas and thus gain necessary understanding. A comprehensive index has been provided for quick access to particular topics, terms and ideas.

Contents

Gradient – Definition

Gradient is a **number** that measures the slope of a line. Divide the **vertical distance** by the **horizontal distance**.

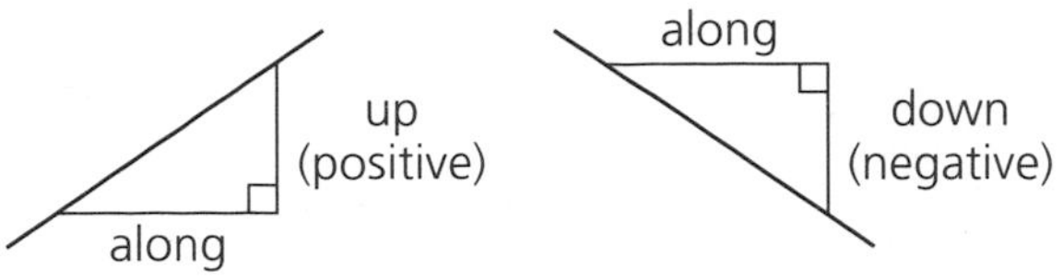

$$\textbf{gradient} = \frac{\textbf{distance up or down}}{\textbf{distance along}}$$

notation

Use m for gradient.

m_{AB} means 'the gradient of line AB'.

$m_{\perp}$ means 'the gradient of a perpendicular line'.

m_1 and m_2 could be used, for example, for the gradient of two different lines.

Gradient Diagram

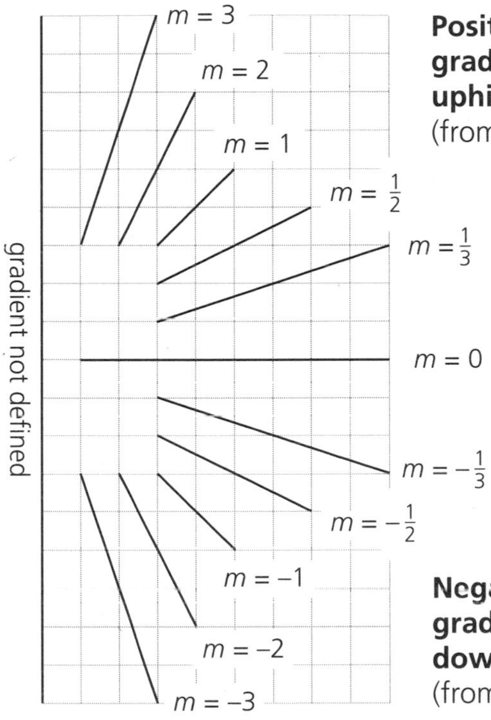

Positive gradients uphill (from left to right)

Negative gradients downhill (from left to right)

Use this diagram to learn to judge a line's gradient from the look of the line.

example 1.1

Estimate the gradient of these lines:

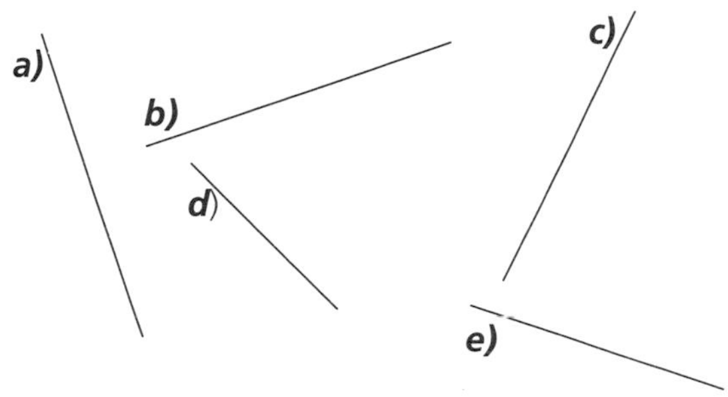

answers: **a)** -3, **b)** $\frac{1}{3}$, **c)** 2, **d)** -1, **e)** $-\frac{1}{3}$

Gradient Formula

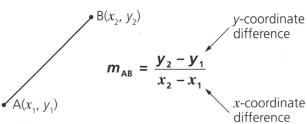

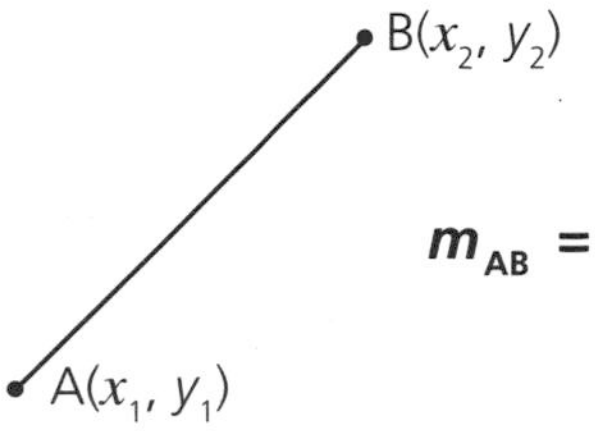

$$m_{AB} = \frac{y_2 - y_1}{x_2 - x_1}$$

y-coordinate difference (top); x-coordinate difference (bottom)

notes:

1. $x_1 \neq x_2$. If $x_1 = x_2$ you get a 'vertical' line which has **no** gradient.

2. $\dfrac{y_1 - y_2}{x_1 - x_2}$ gives the same result.
You can swap **both** top and bottom order but not just one.

example 1.2

Find the gradient of AB where A and B have coordinates (–1, 1) and (5, –2).

solution:

$$m_{AB} = \frac{1-(-2)}{-1-5}$$

(y-coordinate difference on top; x-coordinate difference below)

$$= \frac{3}{-6} = -\frac{1}{2}$$

Note that $\dfrac{-2-1}{5-(-1)} = \dfrac{-3}{6} = -\dfrac{1}{2}$ gives the same result.

1. The Straight Line

Angles and the x-axis

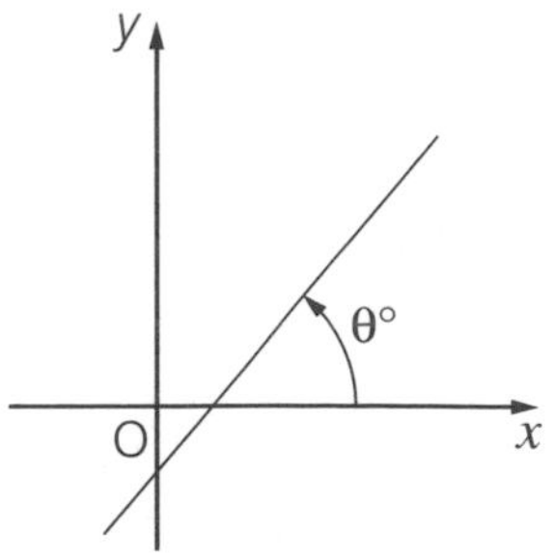

tan θ° is positive
for 0 < θ < 90

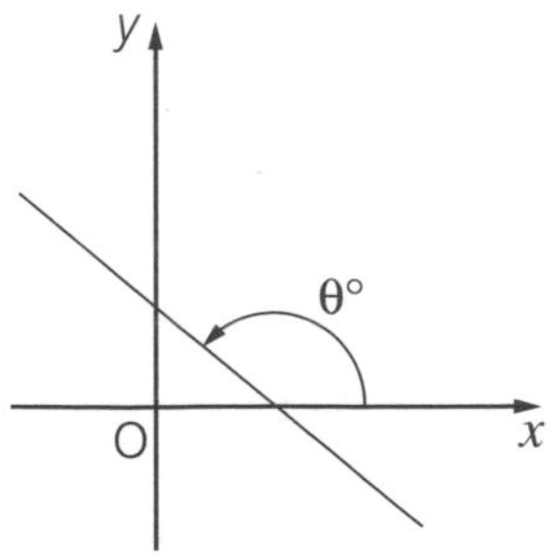

tan θ° is negative
for 90 < θ < 180

Assuming the scales are the same on both axes then...
tan θ = the gradient of the line (*m*)

example 1.3

Find the angle that a line with gradient $-\frac{1}{3}$ makes with the positive direction of the x-axis.

solution:
Suppose the angle is θ°, then...

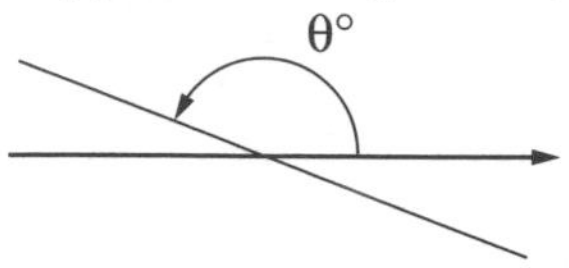

$\tan\theta° = -\frac{1}{3}$
(θ° is in the 2nd quadrant)
(1st quadrant angle is 18·4°)

So θ° = 180° – 18·4° = **161·6°** (to 1 dec. pl.)

Parallel Lines

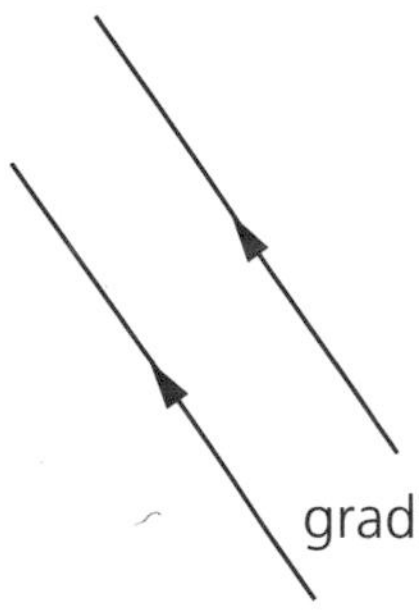

$\boldsymbol{m_1 = m_2}$

If one is true ⇕ then so is the other

The lines are parallel

gradient = m_1

gradient = m_2

example 1.4

For the points A(–1, 2), B(2, –2), C(0, 4) and D(3, 0) show that AB and CD are parallel.

solution: $m_{AB} = \dfrac{2-(-2)}{-1-2} = \dfrac{4}{-3} = -\dfrac{4}{3}$

$m_{CD} = \dfrac{4-0}{0-3} = \dfrac{4}{-3} = -\dfrac{4}{3}$

Since $m_{AB} = m_{CD}$ then AB ll CD.
(AB is parallel to CD.)

Perpendicular Lines

gradient = m_1

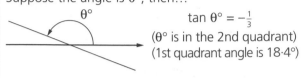

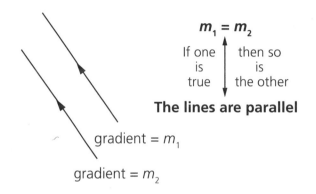

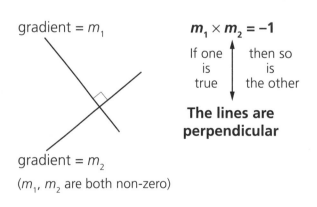

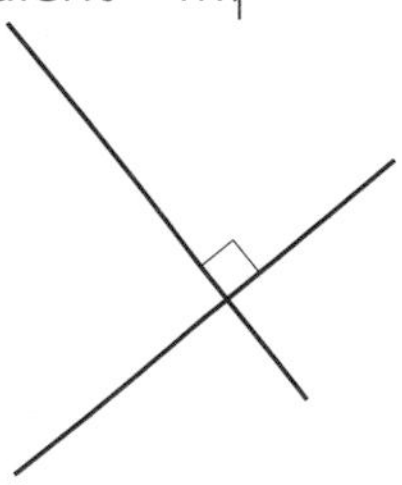

gradient = m_2
(m_1, m_2 are both non-zero)

$\boldsymbol{m_1 \times m_2 = -1}$

If one is true ⇕ then so is the other

The lines are perpendicular

example 1.5

A triangle ABC has vertices A(–3, –1), B(–1, 2) and C(5, –2). Show that it is right-angled.

solution: $m_{AB} = \dfrac{-1-2}{-3-(-1)} = \dfrac{-3}{-2} = \dfrac{3}{2}$

$m_{BC} = \dfrac{2-(-2)}{-1-5} = \dfrac{4}{-6} = -\dfrac{2}{3}$

Since $m_{AB} \times m_{BC} = \frac{3}{2} \times \left(-\frac{2}{3}\right) = -1$

then AB ⊥ BC (AB is perpendicular to BC)
and so ΔABC is right-angled at B.

Perpendicular Gradients

$$\boldsymbol{m = \frac{a}{b} \Rightarrow m_\perp = -\frac{b}{a} \quad (a \neq 0)}$$

change sign and invert

$$\boldsymbol{m = a \Rightarrow m_\perp = -\frac{1}{a} \quad (a \neq 0)}$$

example 1.6

$m = \dfrac{2}{3} \Rightarrow m_\perp = -\dfrac{3}{2}$

$m = -\dfrac{1}{2} \Rightarrow m_\perp = 2$

$m = 3 \Rightarrow m_\perp = -\dfrac{1}{3}$

Recognising a Straight Line Equation

example: $3x - 2y + 5 = 0$

an 'x term' **a 'y term'** — at least one of these is needed

a number — can be missing

> ***example 1.7***
>
> Which of these represent straight line graphs?
>
> ***a)*** $y = 2$ ***b)*** $2x = 4$ ***c)*** $2x^2 - 1 = 0$
>
> ***d)*** $4x - 5y + 1 = 0$ ***e)*** $xy = 2$ ***f)*** $x = y$
>
> *answer:* ***a), b), d)*** and ***f)*** only

Equation of a Line... gradient and y-intercept

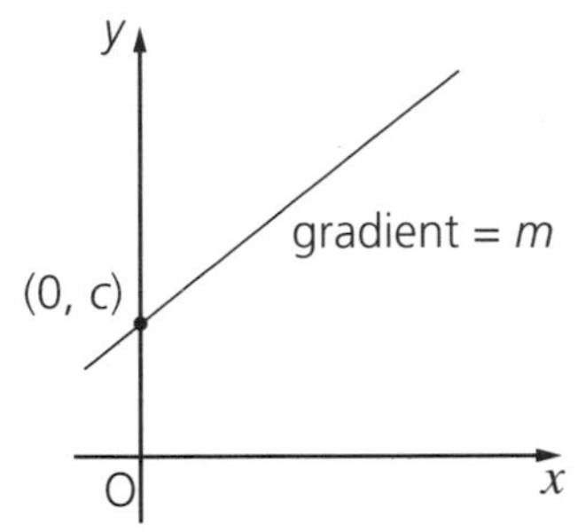

The equation is
$$y = mx + c$$
gradient — m; y-intercept is $(0, c)$

notes:

1. If you are finding the equation of a line and you know...

the gradient m
the y-axis intercept $(0, c)$

then use $y = mx + c$

2. If you are given an equation of a line and you want to know its gradient and y-intercept then **rearrange** the equation to the form $y = mx + c$

> ***example 1.8***
>
> Find the equation of the line perpendicular to $3x - 2y + 4 = 0$ that passes through the origin.
>
> ***solution:***
>
> **step 1** Rearrange to find gradient
> $3x - 2y + 4 = 0$
> $2y = 3x + 4$
> $y = \frac{3}{2}x + 2$ So $m = \frac{3}{2}$ (gradient)
>
> **step 2** Find the perpendicular gradient
> $m = \frac{3}{2} \Rightarrow m_{\perp} = -\frac{2}{3}$ (change sign and invert)
>
> **step 3** Use $y = mx + c$
> $m = -\frac{2}{3}$
> y-intercept is $(0, 0)$
> So $c = 0$
> Equation is $y = -\frac{2}{3}x$ or $3y + 2x = 0$

Special Cases

1.

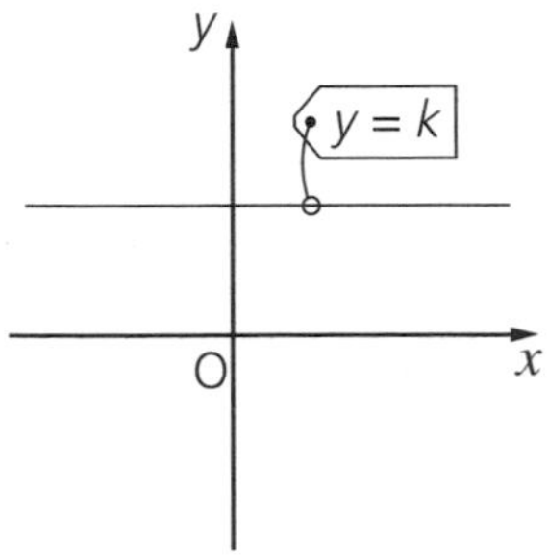

Equations of lines parallel to x-axis are of the form
y = 'a number'

2.

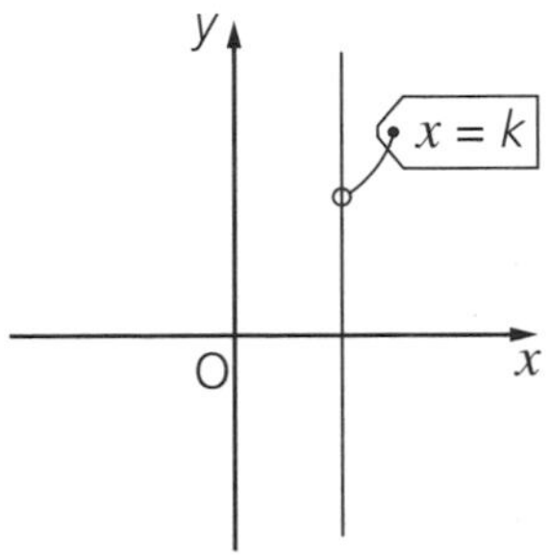

Equations of lines parallel to y-axis are of the form
x = 'a number'

3.

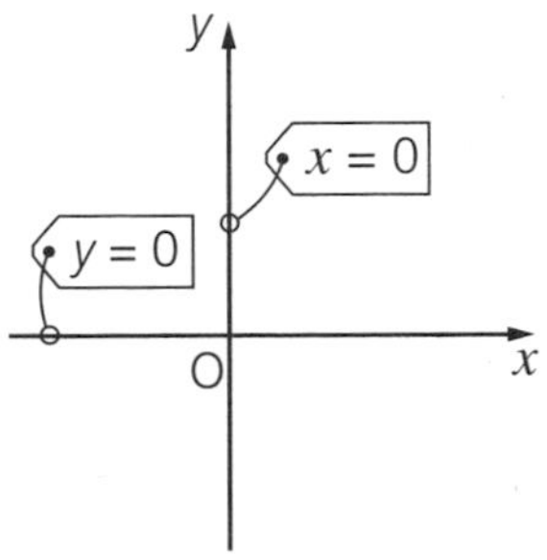

Equation of the x-axis is $\mathbf{y = 0}$

Equation of the y-axis is $\mathbf{x = 0}$

4.

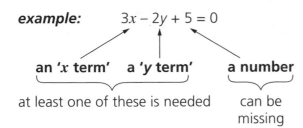

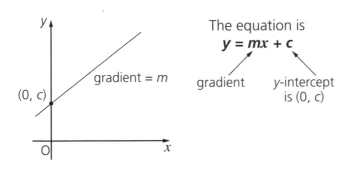

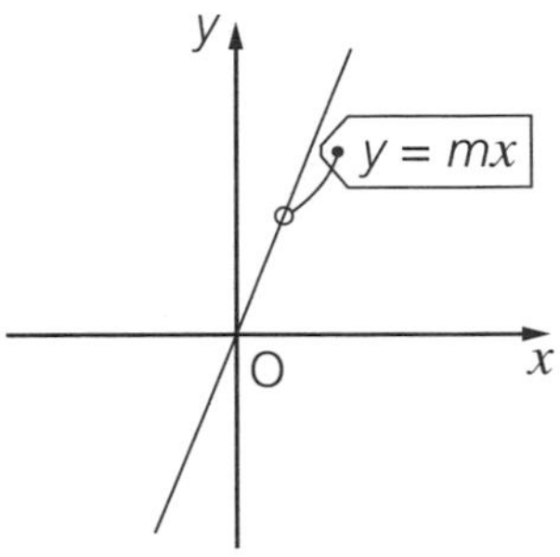

All lines passing through the origin (apart from the y-axis) have equations of the form $\mathbf{y = mx}$

Equation of a Line... gradient and any point

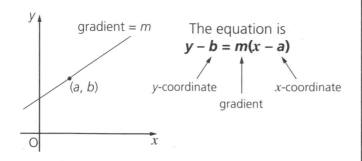

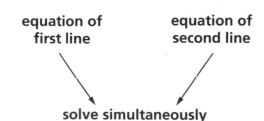

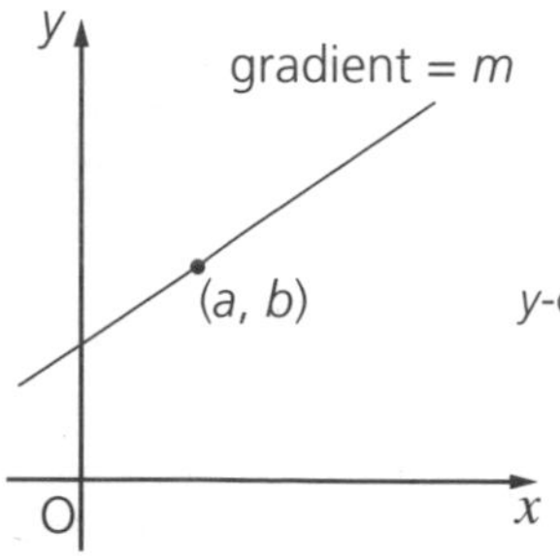

The equation is
$y - b = m(x - a)$

y-coordinate → b; gradient → m; x-coordinate → a

note:
To find the equation of a line you need to know two facts:

fact 1 the gradient: m

fact 2 a point on the line: (a, b)

example 1.9

Find the equation of the line passing through $(2, -3)$ with gradient $\frac{1}{2}$.

solution:
Use $y - b = m(x - a)$
Point on line is $(2, -3)$
Gradient of line is $\frac{1}{2}$

So equation is $y - (-3) = \frac{1}{2}(x - 2)$

$y + 3 = \frac{1}{2}(x - 2)$ ← Get rid of this fraction by doubling

$2y + 6 = x - 2$

$\mathbf{2y - x = -8}$

example 1.10

Find the equation of the line passing through $A(-1, 3)$ and $B(4, -2)$.

solution:

step 1 Find the gradient:

$$m_{AB} = \frac{3-(-2)}{-1-4} = \frac{5}{-5} = -1$$

step 2 Use $y - b = m(x - a)$
Point on line is $(-1, 3)$ Gradient is -1

So equation is $y - 3 = -1(x - (-1))$
$\Rightarrow \quad y - 3 = -(x + 1) \Rightarrow \quad y - 3 = -x - 1$
giving $\mathbf{y + x = 2}$

Where does a line cross the axes?

If you know the equation of the line...

to find: **x-axis intercept** ⟷ **Set $y = 0$ in the equation**

to find: **y-axis intercept** ⟷ **Set $x = 0$ in the equation**

example 1.11

Where does $2y - x = 7$ intersect the axes?

solution:
For x-intercept set $y = 0$ so $2 \times 0 - x = 7$
giving $-x = 7 \Rightarrow x = -7$ Intercept: $\mathbf{(-7, 0)}$

For y-intercept set $x = 0$ so $2y - 0 = 7$
giving $2y = 7 \Rightarrow y = \frac{7}{2}$ Intercept: $\mathbf{\left(0, \frac{7}{2}\right)}$

Where do two lines meet?

equation of first line ↘ **solve simultaneously** ↙ **equation of second line**

example 1.12

Find the point of intersection of the lines $3y = 2x + 4$ and $3x = 7 - 2y$

solution: after rearranging equations

$$\begin{aligned} 3y - 2x &= 4 \;\}\times 3 & \rightarrow \quad 9y - 6x &= 12 \\ 2y + 3x &= 7 \;\}\times 2 & \rightarrow \quad 4y + 6x &= 14 \\ & \text{Add:} & 13y &= 26 \\ & & y &= 2 \end{aligned}$$

Put $y = 2$ in $2y + 3x = 7 \Rightarrow 4 + 3x = 7$
So $3x = 3$ giving $x = 1$
(1, 2) is the point of intersection.

The Distance Formula

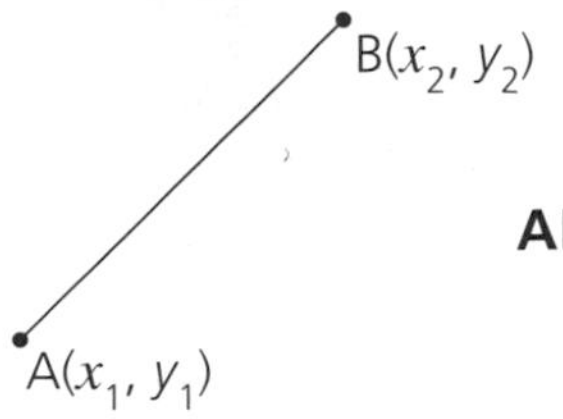

$$AB = \sqrt{(x_2-x_1)^2 + (y_2-y_1)^2}$$

x-coordinate difference y-coordinate difference

note:

$AB^2 = (x_2-x_1)^2 + (y_2-y_1)^2$

if you wish to avoid the square root.

> ***example 1.13***
>
> Show that triangle ABC with vertices A(1, 2), B(3, 0) and C(–1, –2) is isosceles.
>
> ***solution:***
>
> $AC = \sqrt{(1-(-1))^2 + (2-(-2))^2} = \sqrt{2^2 + 4^2}$
> $= \sqrt{4+16} = \sqrt{20}$
>
> $BC = \sqrt{(3-(-1))^2 + (0-(-2))^2} = \sqrt{4^2 + 2^2}$
> $= \sqrt{16+4} = \sqrt{20}$
>
> So AC = BC and the triangle is isosceles.

The Midpoint Formula

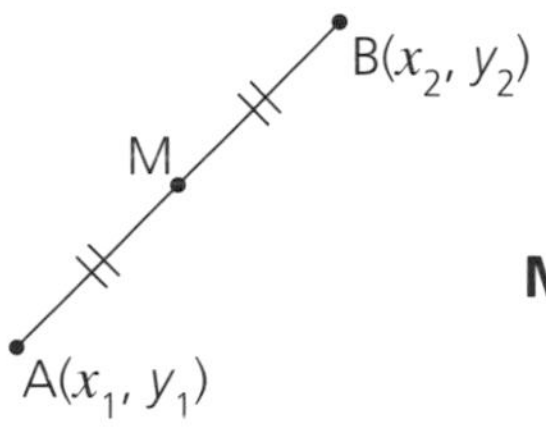

$$M\left(\frac{x_1+x_2}{2}, \frac{y_1+y_2}{2}\right)$$

'average' of the x-coordinates   'average' of the y-coordinates

> ***example 1.14***
>
> Find the coordinates of M, the midpoint of CD, where C is the point (–1, 5) and D is (–5, 2).
>
> ***solution:***
>
> $M\left(\frac{-1+(-5)}{2}, \frac{5+2}{2}\right)$
>
> $= M\left(\frac{-6}{2}, \frac{7}{2}\right) = M\left(-3, \frac{7}{2}\right)$

Special Lines in a Triangle

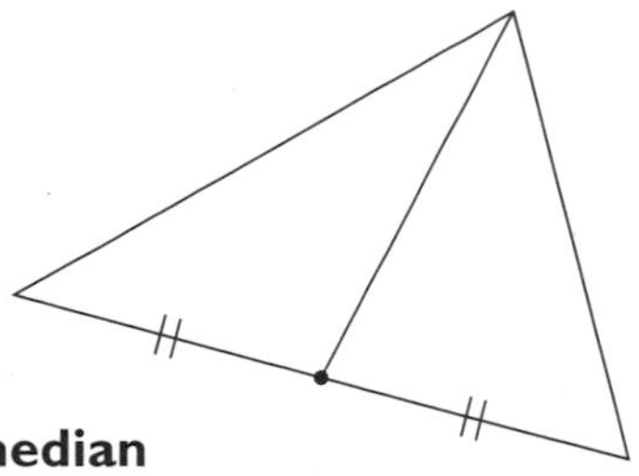

A **median** joins a vertex to the midpoint of the opposite side.

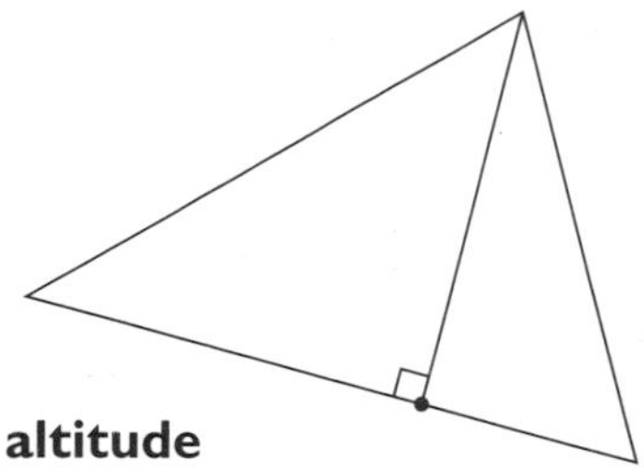

An **altitude** is a line through a vertex perpendicular to the opposite side.

An **angle bisector**

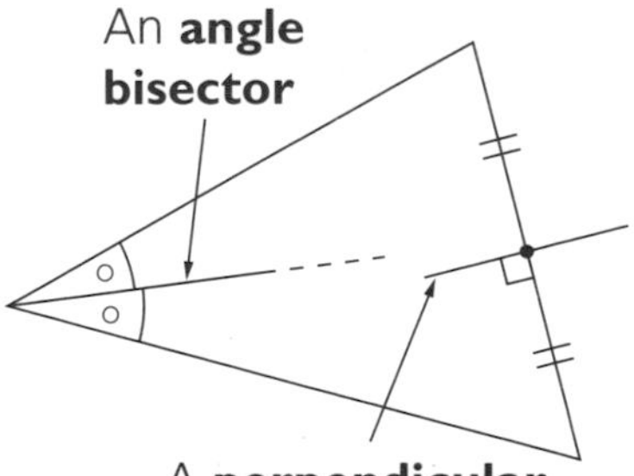

A **perpendicular bisector** of a side.

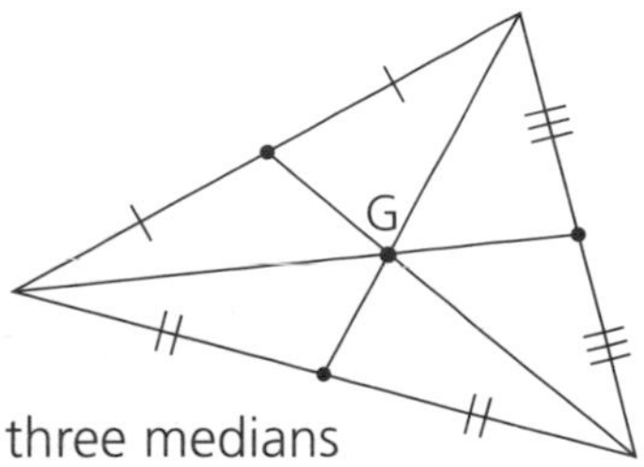

The three medians are **concurrent**. They meet at G, the **centroid** of the triangle.

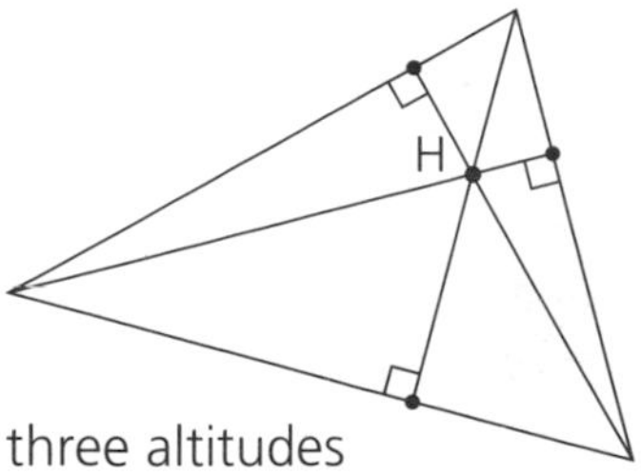

The three altitudes are also concurrent (meeting at H, the **orthocentre**).

notes:

1. The centroid G divides each median in the ratio 2:1 (vertex to midpoint).

2. 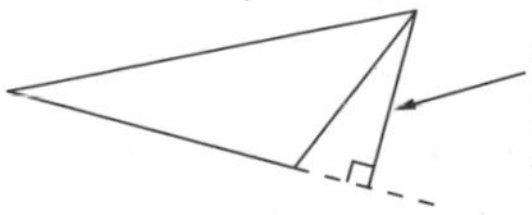 Altitudes can lie 'outside' the triangle.

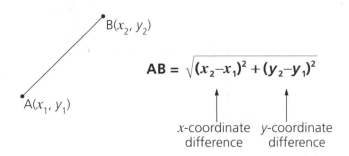

3. The three angle bisectors are concurrent as are the three perpendicular bisectors of the sides.

1. The Straight Line

Locus

The set of all the possible positions of a point satisfying a given condition is called the **locus** of that point.

example 1.15

Find the equation of the locus of a point that is equidistant from the x- and y-axes.

solution:
Every point on the line $y = x$ and the line $y = -x$ is the same distance from the x-axis as it is from the y-axis.

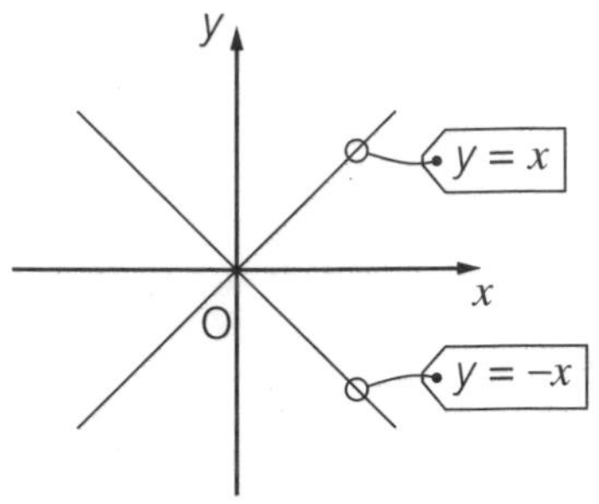

2. Numbers, Sets and Notation

Set Notation

Sets are collections of things, usually numbers. The **members** or **elements** of a set are **listed** or **described** inside 'curly brackets' **{ }**.

$\in$ means 'is a member of'.

$\notin$ means 'is not a member of'.

The **Empty Set** is the set with no members.

A collection of only some of the members of a given set is called a **subset** of that set.

Sets of Numbers

You will need to recognise the following sets of numbers:

N = {**Natural Numbers**} = {1, 2, 3, 4, ...}

W = {**Whole Numbers**} = {0, 1, 2, 3, ...}

Z = {**Integers**} = {..., −3, −2, −1, 0, 1, 2, 3, ...}
(−3, −2, −1: Negative Integers; 1, 2, 3: Positive Integers)

Q = {**Rational Numbers**}
These are numbers that can be written as a 'Ratio' of two integers, eg $\frac{2}{3}$, $-4 = \frac{-4}{1}$, $1{\cdot}25 = \frac{5}{4}$

R = {**Real Numbers**}
These are numbers that can be represented by **all** the points on the Real Number line.
eg:

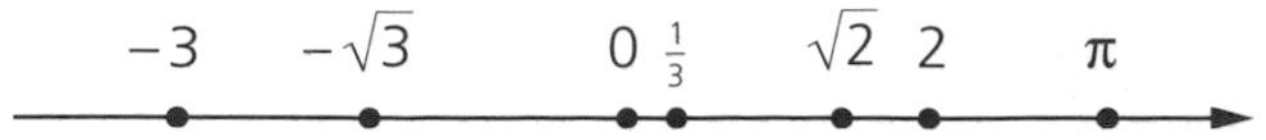

note:

N is a subset of **W**, **W** is a subset of **Z**, **Z** is a subset of **Q**, **Q** is a subset of **R**.

examples:

$2 \in$ **N**. This means '2 is a Natural Number'.

The Even Numbers and the Odd Numbers are subsets of the Natural Numbers.

$1 \notin$ {Primes}. This means '1 is not a Prime Number'.

The set of solutions from **R** of $x^2 = -4$ is the Empty Set. In other words the equation has no Real solutions.

What is a Function?

A function, f, consists of:

1. a **formula**, $f(x)$, which tells you what to do with a given value of x.
2. a **domain** which describes the values of x you are allowed to use in the formula.

note: When considering the domain of a given function **avoid** numbers that will cause:
- Division by zero
- Square-rooting a negative number.

domain   range

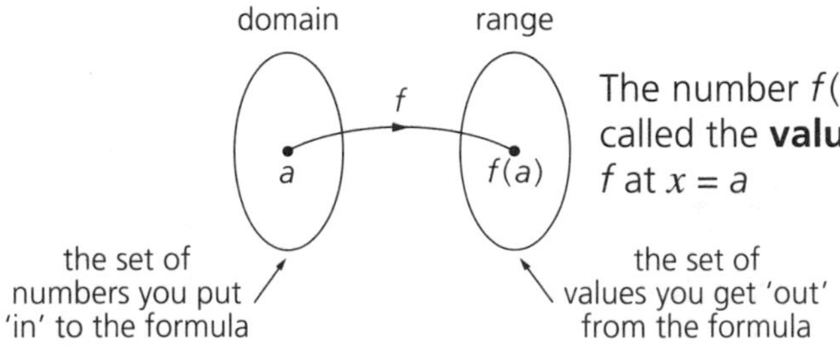

The number $f(a)$ is called the **value** of f at $x = a$

the set of numbers you put 'in' to the formula

the set of values you get 'out' from the formula

Function Graphs

A typical **graph** of a function f shows the points $(a, f(a))$ for all values $x = a$ in the domain of f.

range ('out' numbers)

$f(a)$

$(a, f(a))$

$y = f(x)$

domain ('in' numbers)

---

example 3.1

Describe a suitable domain for the functions defined by:

a) $f(x) = \dfrac{x+1}{x^2+x-6}$ **b)** $g(x) = \sqrt{x-3}$

solution:

a) Avoid $x^2 + x - 6 = 0$
$$(x - 2)(x + 3) = 0$$
$$x = 2 \text{ or } x = -3$$
A suitable domain is: all real numbers apart from -3 and 2

b) Avoid $x - 3 < 0$ so avoid $x < 3$
A suitable domain is: all real numbers $x \geq 3$

Graphs of Related Functions

$y = f(x + k)$ shifts the graph $y = f(x)$ k units to the left.

$y = (x + k)^2$

$y = f(x - k)$ shifts the graph $y = f(x)$ k units to the right.

$y = (x - k)^2$

$y = -f(x)$ 'flips' the graph $y = f(x)$ in the x-axis.

$y = -x^2$

$y = kf(x)$ 'stretches' the graph along the y-axis if $k > 1$. The heights on the graph are multiplied by k.

$y = kx^2$

Start with the graph $y = f(x)$

$y = x^2$

$y = f(x) - k$ shifts the graph $y = f(x)$ down k units.

$y = x^2 - k$

$y = kf(x)$ 'squashes' the graph along the y-axis if $0 < k < 1$. The heights on the graph are multiplied by k.

$y = kx^2$

$y = f(x) + k$ shifts the graph $y = f(x)$ up k units.

$y = x^2 + k$

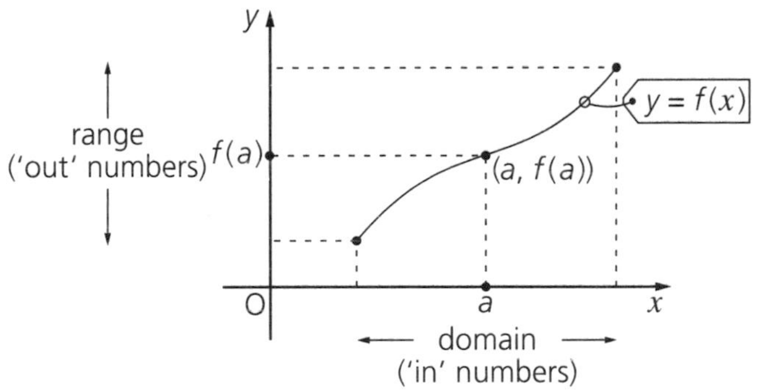

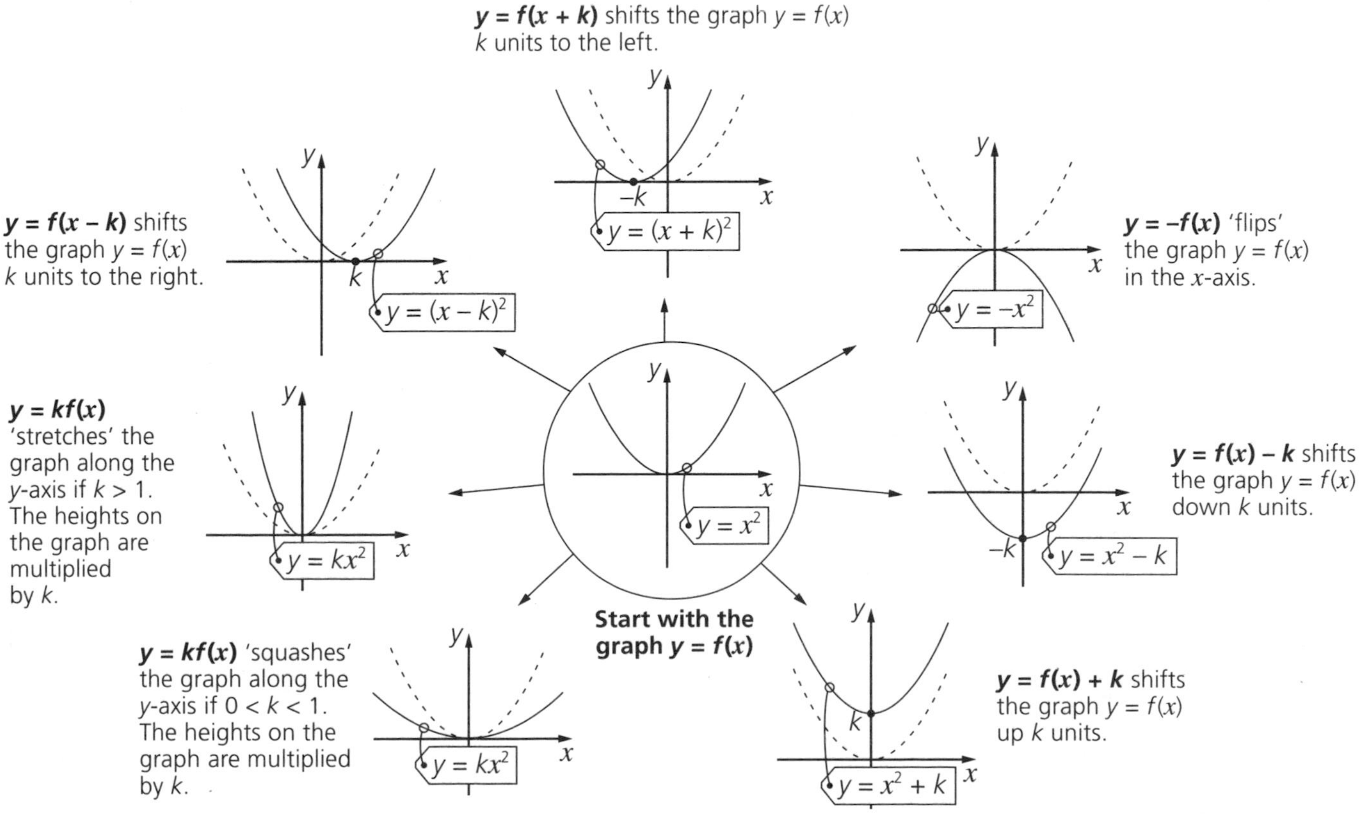

example 3.2

The graph of $y = f(x)$ is shown:

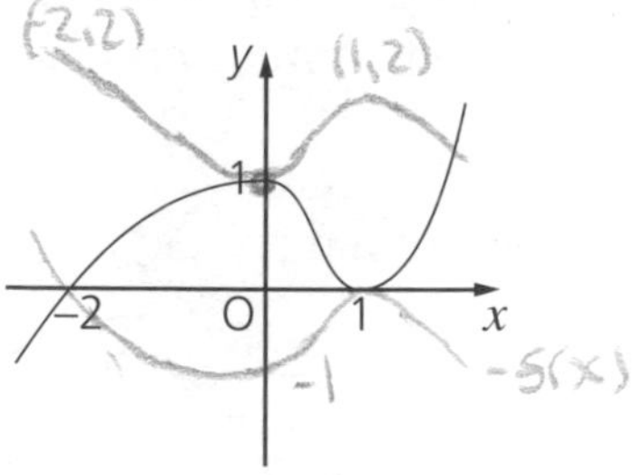

Sketch the graph $y = 2 - f(x)$

solution: Split into two steps:

step 1 graph of $y = -f(x)$

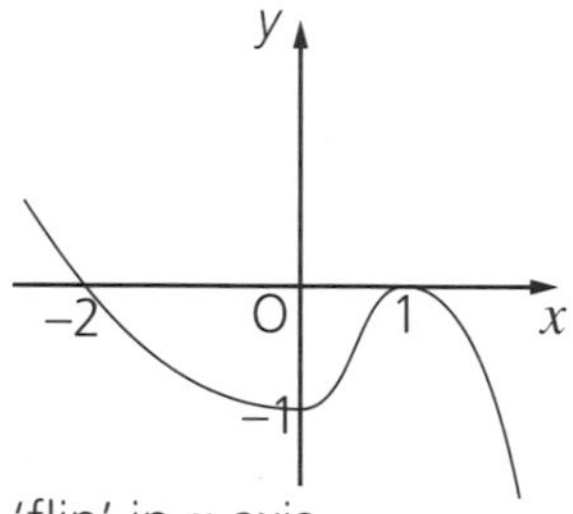

'flip' in x-axis

step 2 graph of $y = 2 - f(x)$

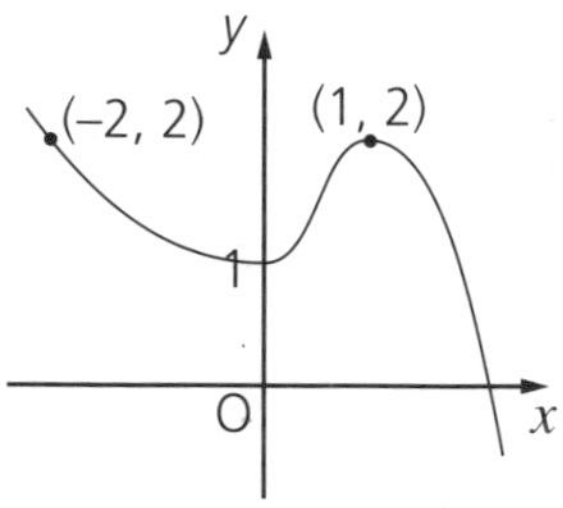

shift up 2 units

example 3.3

The sketch shows the graph $y = a(x - b)^2 - c$

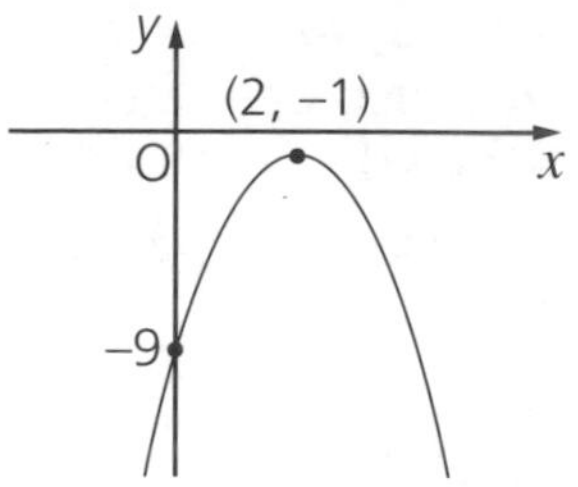

Find the values of a, b and c.

solution:

Start with $y = x^2$. 'Flip' in the x-axis, so value of a is negative.

Then move graph 2 units right, $\mathbf{b = 2}$, and 1 unit down, $\mathbf{c = 1}$

This gives $y = a(x - 2)^2 - 1$.

Since $x = 0$ gives $y = -9$ (y-intercept)
then $-9 = a(0 - 2)^2 - 1$ so $-9 = 4a - 1$
so $4a = -8$ giving $\mathbf{a = -2}$

Composite Functions

Two functions f and g can be combined 'one after the other':

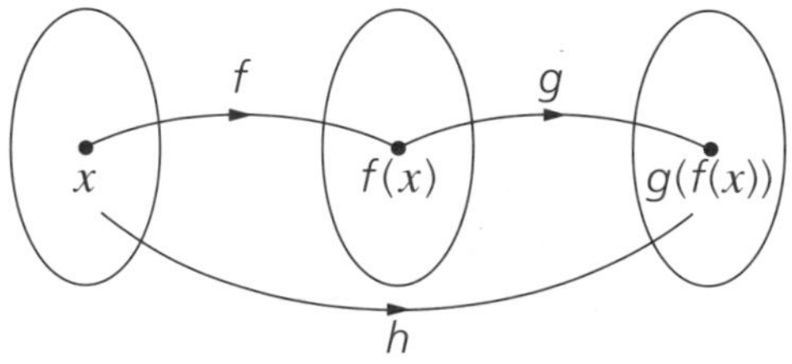

This gives a new function h defined by
$\mathbf{h(x) = g(f(x))}$

example 3.4

If $f(x) = 2x - 1$ and $g(x) = 3x^2$, find $f(g(x))$ and $g(f(x))$ and show $g(f(x)) - 2f(g(x)) = 5 - 12x$

solution:

$f(g(x)) = f(3x^2) = 2(3x^2) - 1 = \mathbf{6x^2 - 1}$

$g(f(x)) = g(2x - 1) = 3(2x - 1)^2 = \mathbf{12x^2 - 12x + 3}$

So $g(f(x)) - 2f(g(x))$
$= 12x^2 - 12x + 3 - 2(6x^2 - 1)$
$= 12x^2 - 12x + 3 - 12x^2 + 2 = \mathbf{5 - 12x}$

Inverse Functions

A function f can have an inverse $\boldsymbol{f^{-1}}$ which 'undoes' f:

$$f^{-1}(f(a)) = a$$

for all values $x = a$ in the domain of f.

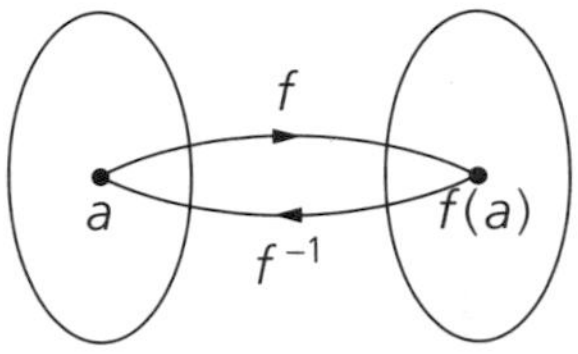

Graphs and Inverses

Function Graph
$\boldsymbol{y = f(x)}$

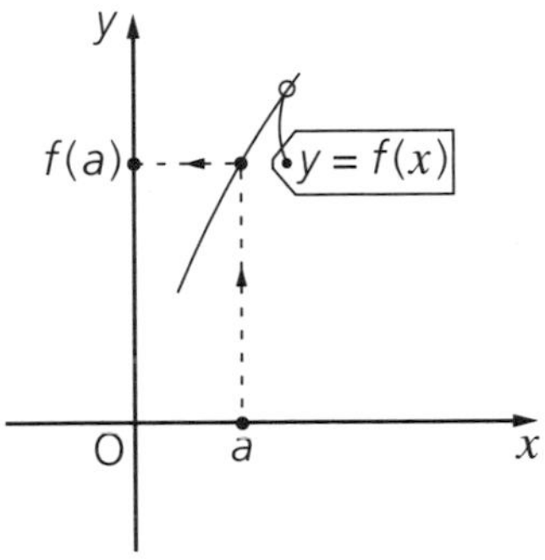

reverse the process ⟹ 'flip' in the line $y = x$

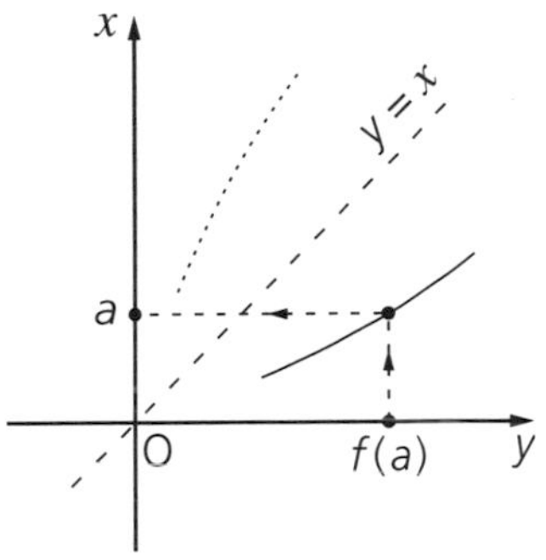

relabel ⟹ the axes

Inverse Function Graph
$\boldsymbol{y = f^{-1}(x)}$

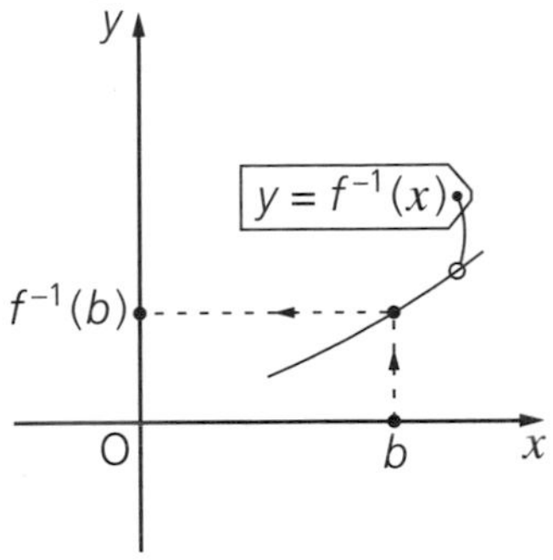

a goes 'in'. $f(a)$ comes 'out'.

$f(a)$ goes 'in'. a comes 'out'.

If $f(a) = b$ then $a = f^{-1}(b)$.

example 3.5

Here are three examples of inverse functions and their graphs:

Doubling
$f(x) = 2x$

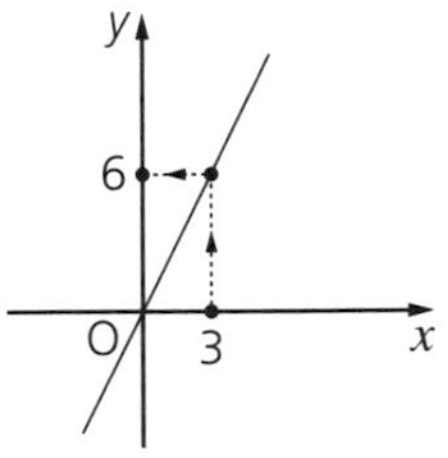

⇓

Halving
$f^{-1}(x) = \frac{1}{2}x$

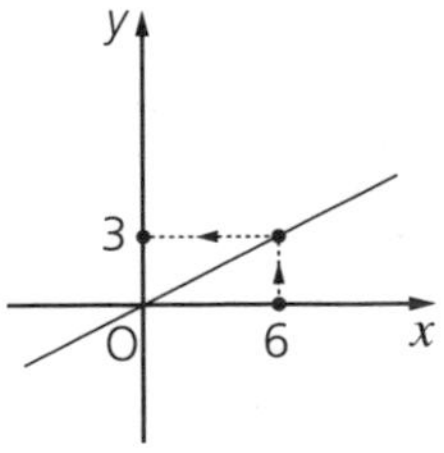

Squaring
$f(x) = x^2 \ (x \geq 0)$

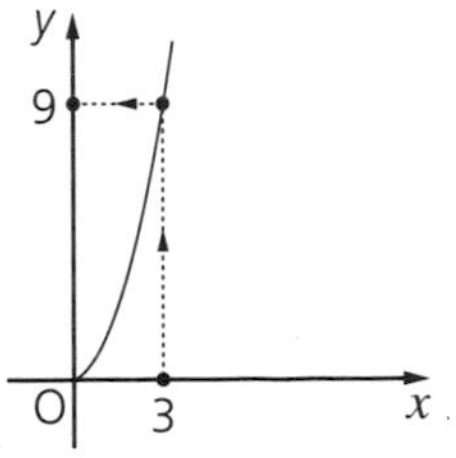

⇓

Square-rooting
$f^{-1}(x) = \sqrt{x} \ \ (x \geq 0)$

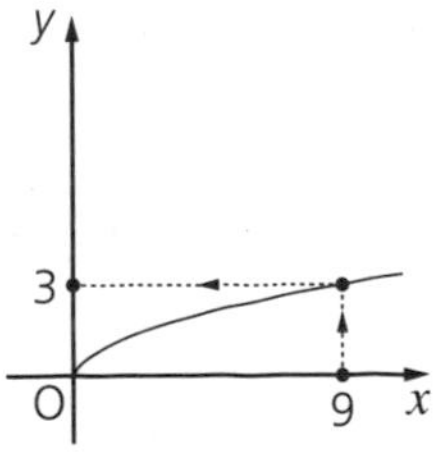

Inverting
$f(x) = \frac{1}{x} \ \ (x \neq 0)$

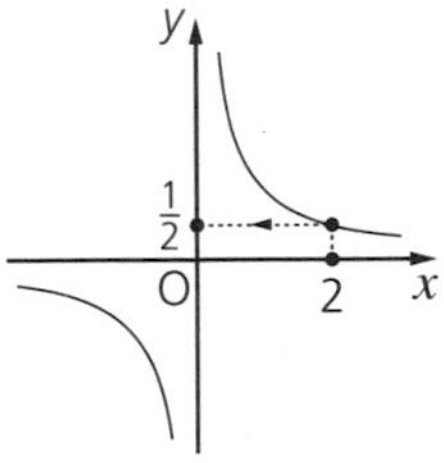

⇓

Inverting
$f^{-1}(x) = \frac{1}{x} \ \ (x \neq 0)$

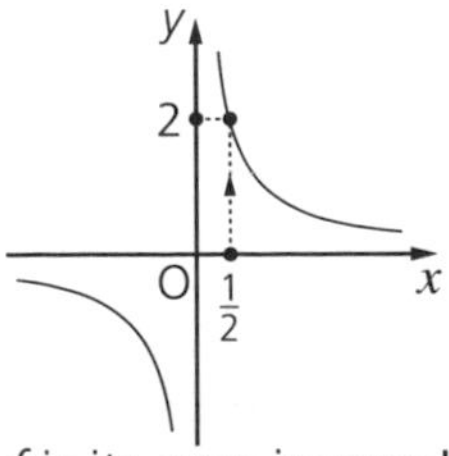

f is its own inverse!

3. Functions and Graphs

Exponential Functions

The functions defined by $f(x) = a^x$ are called **exponential functions**.
When $a > 1$ they are **growth functions**.

one example:

'The powers of 2'
$y = 2^x$

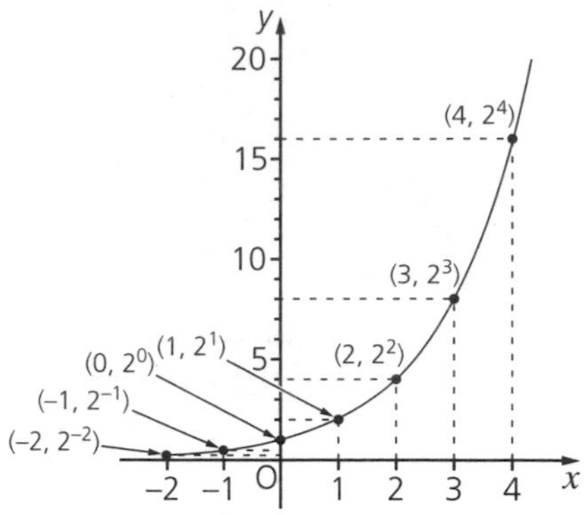

other examples:

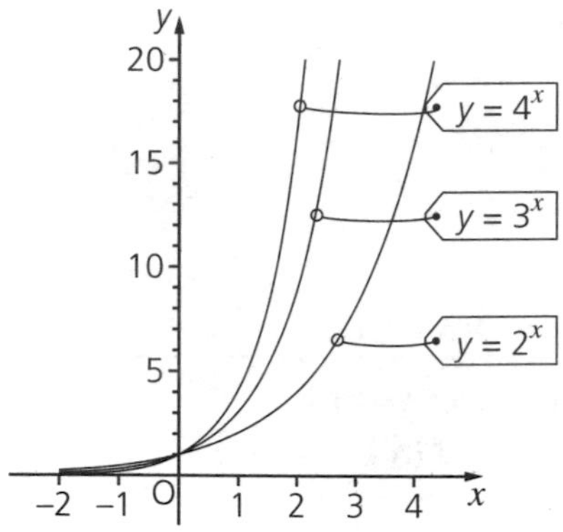

When $0 < a < 1$ they are **decay functions**.

one example:

'The powers of $\frac{1}{2}$'
$y = \left(\frac{1}{2}\right)^x = 2^{-x}$

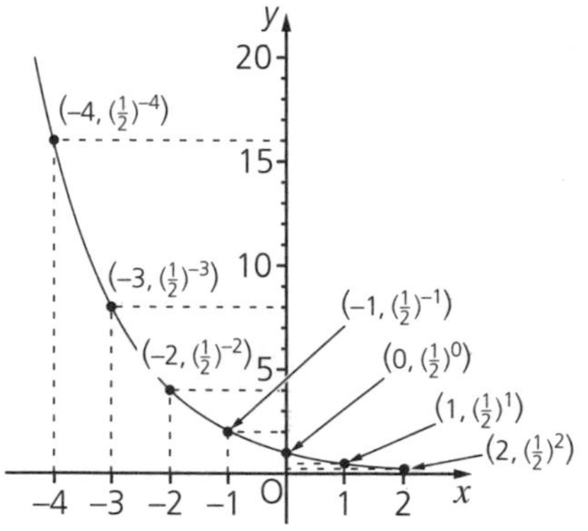

other examples:

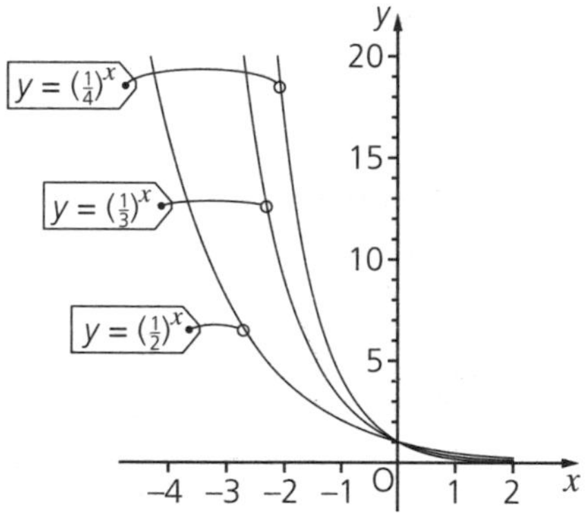

notes:

1. $y = \left(\frac{1}{2}\right)^x = \frac{1}{2^x} = 2^{-x}$; $y = \left(\frac{1}{3}\right)^x = \frac{1}{3^x} = 3^{-x}$; $y = \left(\frac{1}{4}\right)^x = 4^{-x}$... etc

2. These exponential graphs all lie above the x-axis, ie $y = a^x > 0$ (a^x is positive).

The Inverse of '2 to the power of...'

(Exponential)
Function Graph

(Logarithmic)
Inverse Function Graph

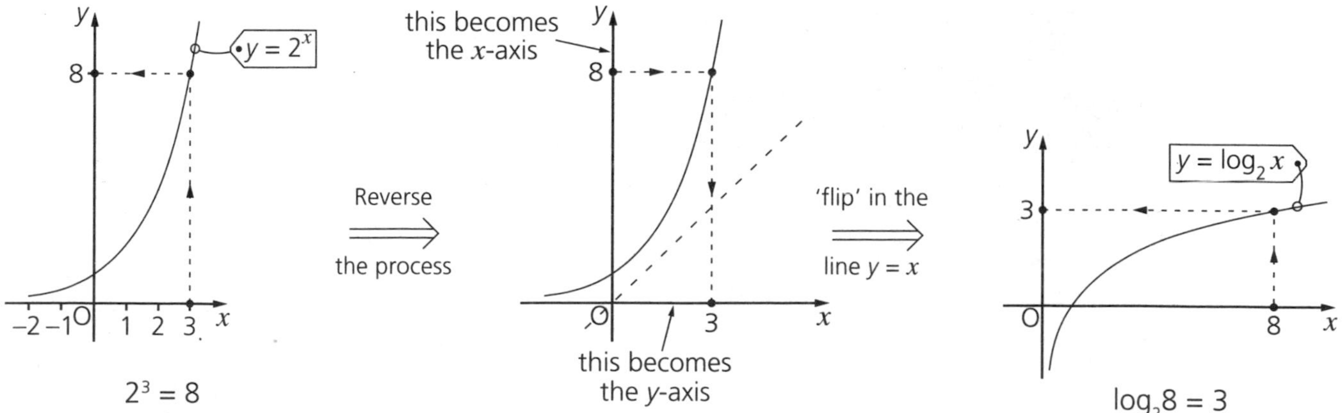

$2^3 = 8$
'2 to the power of...'

$\log_2 8 = 3$
'log to the base 2 of...'

The Logarithmic Function

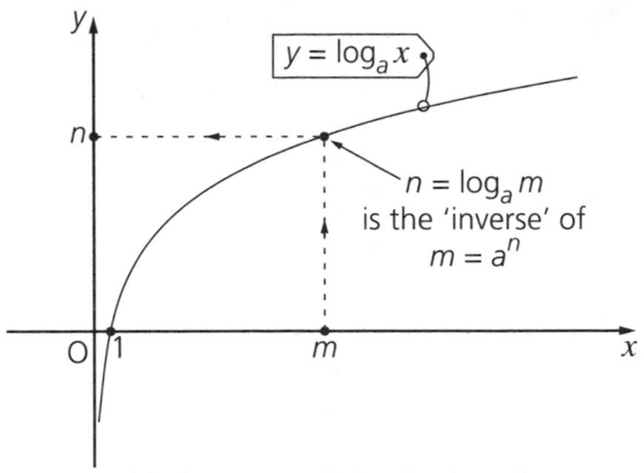

This is a **Logarithmic Graph**.

notes:

1. a is the **base**. The log graph shown has $a > 1$.

2. log graphs pass through (1, 0)
$0 = \log_a 1 \longleftrightarrow a^0 = 1$

3. $\log_a x$ is only defined for $x > 0$ (powers of a only give positive answers... think about it!)

example 3.6

This is a sketch of part of the graph of $y = \log_3 x$

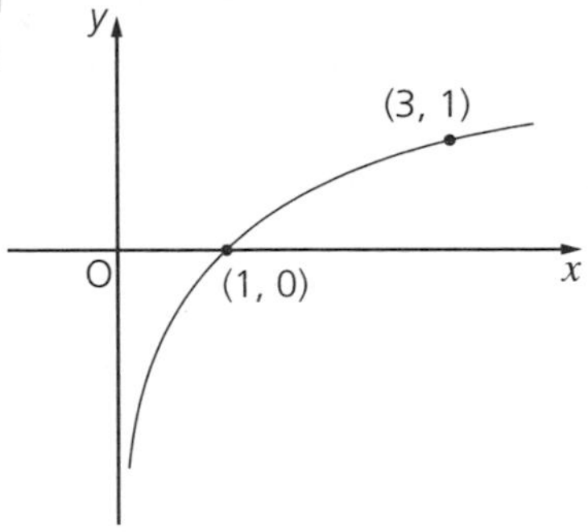

Sketch the graph $y = \log_3(x + 3) + 1$

solution: $y = \log_3(x + 3) + 1$

Move the given graph 3 units left; Then move graph up 1 unit

Here is the resulting graph...
(3, 1) ⟶ (0, 2)
(1, 0) ⟶ (−2, 1)

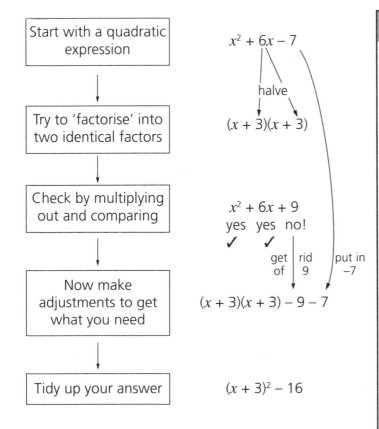

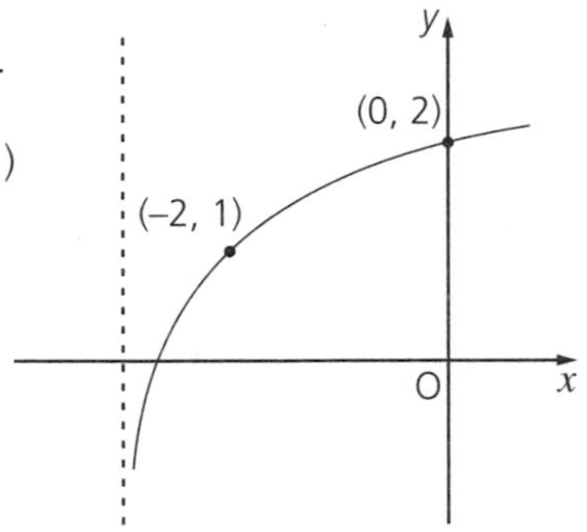

Quadratic Functions... Completing the Square

The Method

Start with a quadratic expression	$x^2 + 6x - 7$
Try to 'factorise' into two identical factors	halve: $(x + 3)(x + 3)$
Check by multiplying out and comparing	$x^2 + 6x + 9$ yes ✓ yes ✓ no!
Now make adjustments to get what you need	get rid of 9, put in −7: $(x + 3)(x + 3) - 9 - 7$
Tidy up your answer	$(x + 3)^2 - 16$

note: You recognise these questions by:
'express in the form $(x + a)^2 + b$' or
'express in the form $a - (x + b)^2$' etc.

example 3.7

Express $3 + 8x - 2x^2$ in the form $a + b(x + c)^2$ where a, b and c are constants.

solution:

Rewrite in 'normal' order	$3 + 8x - 2x^2$ $= -2x^2 + 8x + 3$
'Force out' a common factor to get x^2	$= -2[x^2 - 4x - \frac{3}{2}]$
Proceed as normal getting equal factors and making adjustments	$= -2[(x - 2)(x - 2) - 4 - \frac{3}{2}]$ $= -2[(x - 2)^2 - \frac{11}{2}]$
Multiply out	$= -2(x - 2)^2 + 11$
Tidy up	$= \mathbf{11 - 2(x - 2)^2}$

Sketching Quadratic Graphs

hints:

$$y = ax^2 + bx + c$$

If $a > 0$ then the parabola is concave upwards.

If $a < 0$ then the parabola is concave downwards.

Where does it cross the y-axis? ⟶ Set $x = 0$ to find y

Where does it cross the x-axis? ⟶ Set $y = 0$ and solve the equation

Complete the square: $y = (x + d)^2 + e$

So move the graph $y = x^2$ d units left and up e units.

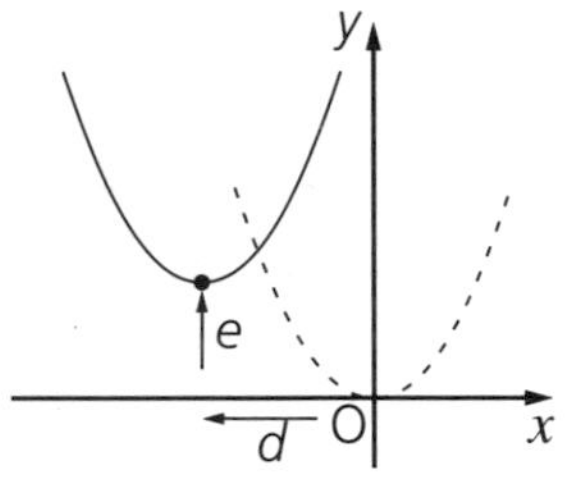

example 3.8

Sketch $y = x^2 - 6x + 10$ and give the coordinates of the minimum turning point.

solution: When $x = 0$, $y = 10$
so the y-intercept is (0, 10)

Also $y = x^2 - 6x + 10 = (x - 3)^2 + 1$
So $y = x^2$ is moved 3 right and 1 up.

The minimum turning point is **(3, 1)**

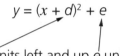

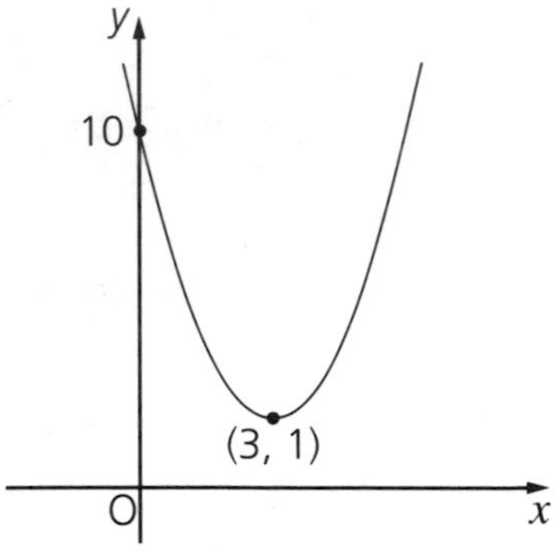

What is a Radian?

Lay a radius-length along the circumference of any circle. Then the angle formed at the centre is 1 radian.

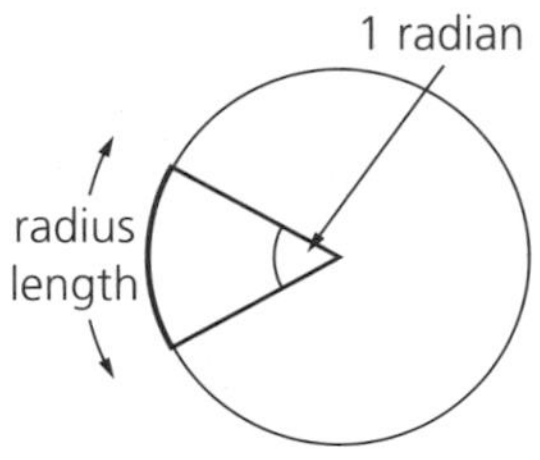

Since circumference = $2\pi r$
then semicircle = πr
So π radius-lengths make up a semicircle.

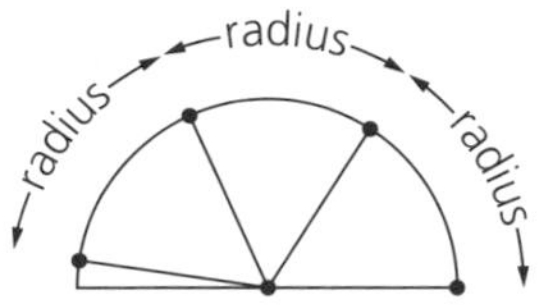

Looking at the angles formed at the centre
π radians = 180°

Some Exact Values

For $\frac{\pi}{4}$ or 45° use half a square of side 1:

For $\frac{\pi}{6}$, $\frac{\pi}{3}$ or 30°, 60° use half an equilateral triangle of side 2:

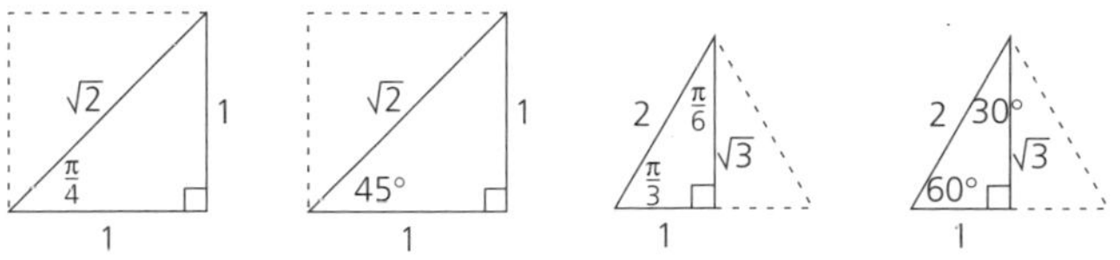

Now use 'SOHCAHTOA' to find **exact** values:

$\sin\frac{\pi}{4} = \frac{1}{\sqrt{2}}$	$\sin 45° = \frac{1}{\sqrt{2}}$	$\sin\frac{\pi}{6} = \frac{1}{2}$	$\sin 30° = \frac{1}{2}$	$\sin\frac{\pi}{3} = \frac{\sqrt{3}}{2}$	$\sin 60° = \frac{\sqrt{3}}{2}$
$\cos\frac{\pi}{4} = \frac{1}{\sqrt{2}}$	$\cos 45° = \frac{1}{\sqrt{2}}$	$\cos\frac{\pi}{6} = \frac{\sqrt{3}}{2}$	$\cos 30° = \frac{\sqrt{3}}{2}$	$\cos\frac{\pi}{3} = \frac{1}{2}$	$\cos 60° = \frac{1}{2}$
$\tan\frac{\pi}{4} = 1$	$\tan 45° = 1$	$\tan\frac{\pi}{6} = \frac{1}{\sqrt{3}}$	$\tan 30° = \frac{1}{\sqrt{3}}$	$\tan\frac{\pi}{3} = \sqrt{3}$	$\tan 60° = \sqrt{3}$

For 0, $\frac{\pi}{2}$, π, $\frac{3\pi}{2}$, 2π or 0°, 90°, 180°, 270°, 360° use:

The Sine Graph

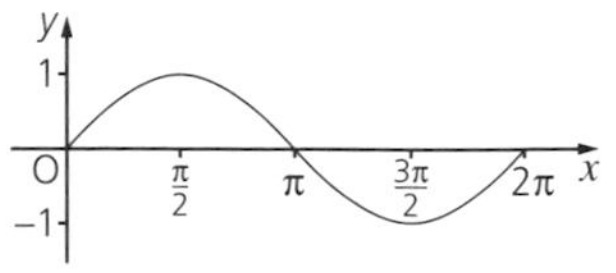

The Cosine Graph

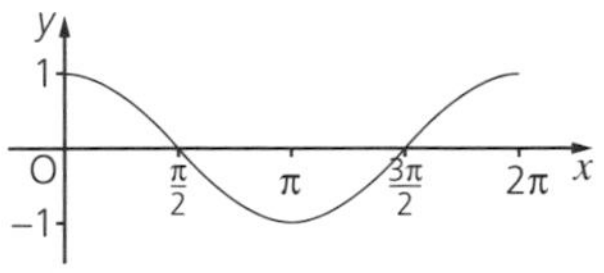

Reading from the graphs gives:

$\sin 0 = 0$ $\quad \sin\frac{\pi}{2} = 1$ $\quad \cos 0 = 1$ $\quad \cos\frac{\pi}{2} = 0$

$\sin \pi = 0$ $\quad \sin\frac{3\pi}{2} = -1$ $\quad \cos \pi = -1$ $\quad \cos\frac{3\pi}{2} = 0$

$\sin 2\pi = 0$ $\quad \cos 2\pi = 1$

Some Trig Formulae

$$\frac{\sin\theta}{\cos\theta} = \tan\theta$$

$$\sin^2\theta + \cos^2\theta = 1$$

rearranging gives

$$\sin^2\theta = 1 - \cos^2\theta$$

$$\cos^2\theta = 1 - \sin^2\theta$$

Useful Conversions

radians		degrees
π	⟷	180°
$\frac{\pi}{6}$	⟷	30°
$\frac{\pi}{4}$	⟷	45°
$\frac{\pi}{3}$	⟷	60°
$\frac{\pi}{2}$	⟷	90°
$\frac{3\pi}{2}$	⟷	270°
2π	⟷	360°

Using the Calculator

When working with

sin cos tan

sin⁻¹ cos⁻¹ tan⁻¹

For degrees
(D or DEG on display) mode 4

For radians
(R or RAD on display) mode 5

example 4.1

a) Find the exact value of $1 - \sin^2\frac{\pi}{4}$

solution: $1 - \sin^2\frac{\pi}{4}$

$= 1 - \left(\frac{1}{\sqrt{2}}\right)^2$

$= 1 - \frac{1}{2} = \mathbf{\frac{1}{2}}$

b) Solve $\sin x° = \frac{\sqrt{3}}{2}$ for $0 \le x \le 90$

solution:
This is an exact value in the 1st quadrant only so $\boldsymbol{x = 60}$

c) Solve $\sin x = 0{\cdot}3$ for $0 \le x \le \frac{\pi}{2}$

solution:
Put calculator into 'Radian Mode' (mode 5) and enter 0·3. Now use sin⁻¹ giving
$\boldsymbol{x = 0{\cdot}305}$ (to 3 sig. figs.)
radians

Warning
Return your calculator immediately to 'Degree Mode' (mode 4) ready for working in degrees.

4. Trigonometry – Basic Facts

Sketching Trig Graphs

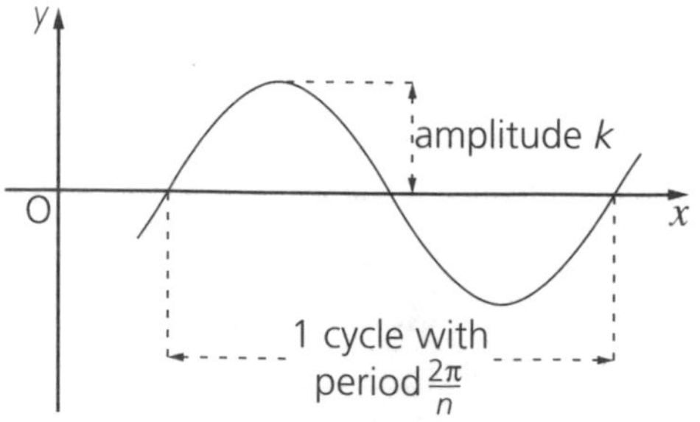

For graphs $y = k \sin nx$ and $y = k \cos nx$ with $k > 0$ and $n > 0$...

...the **amplitude** is k. The maximum value on the graph is k and the minimum is $-k$.

...the **number of cycles** for $0 \leq x \leq 2\pi$ is n

with each cycle having a **period** of $\frac{2\pi}{n}$

Solving Trig Equations

step 1 Rearrange to get $\begin{matrix}\text{sin/cos}\\\text{or tan}\end{matrix}$ (angle) = number

step 2 Determine which quadrants the angle is in. Use the sign of the number and the Quadrant Diagram:

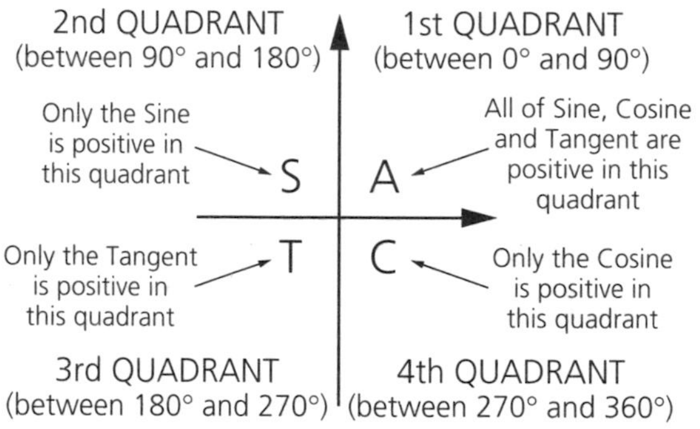

step 3 Find the 1st Quadrant angle (use exact values or inverse trig key) using the **positive** value of the number.

step 4 Calculate the required angles using this diagram:

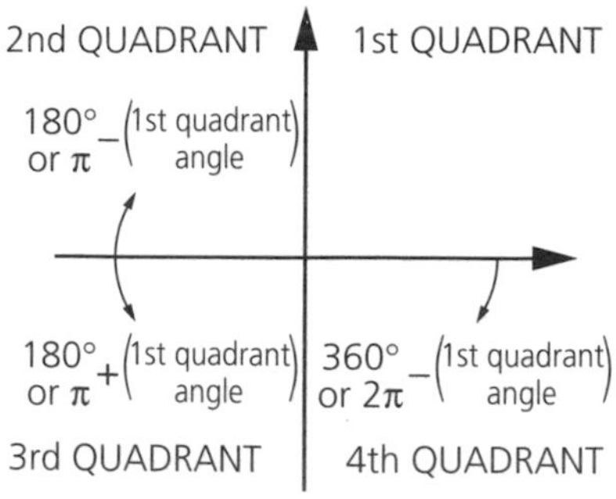

---

example 4.2

Sketch: ***a)*** $y = 2\sin x$ ***b)*** $y = \frac{1}{2}\sin 2x$ ***c)*** $y = 3\cos\frac{1}{2}x$

solution:

a)

Amplitude = 2

1 cycle; period $\frac{2\pi}{1} = 2\pi$

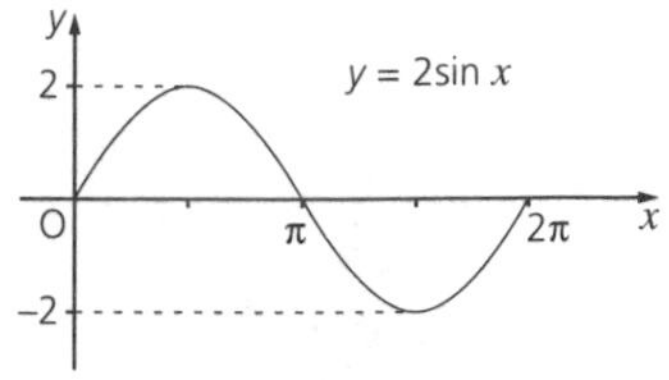

b)

Amplitude = $\frac{1}{2}$

2 cycles; period $\frac{2\pi}{2} = \pi$

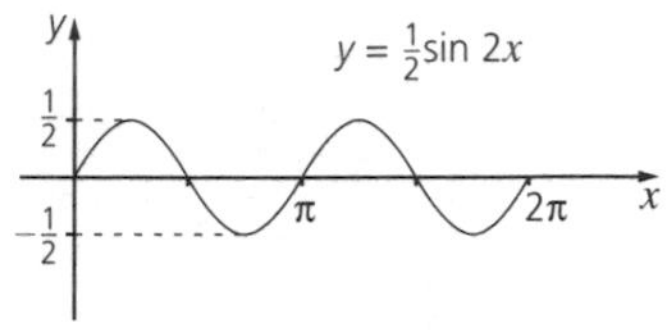

c)

Amplitude = 3

$\frac{1}{2}$ cycle; period $\frac{2\pi}{\frac{1}{2}} = 4\pi$

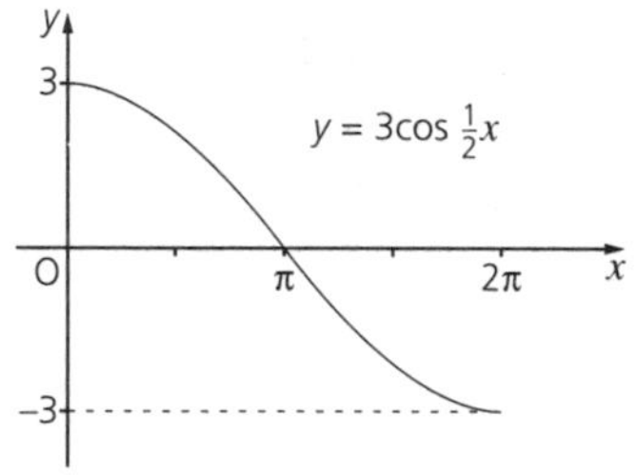

---

example 4.3

Solve: $2\sin x + 1 = 0, 0 \leq x < 2\pi$

solution:

step 1 $2\sin x + 1 = 0$ rearranges to $\sin x = -\frac{1}{2}$

step 2 $\sin x$ is negative for angles in the 3rd or 4th quadrants

step 3 1st quadrant angle is $\frac{\pi}{6}$ (since $\sin\frac{\pi}{6} = \frac{1}{2}$)

step 4

$x = \pi + \frac{\pi}{6}$	or	$x = 2\pi - \frac{\pi}{6}$
(3rd quadrant)		(4th quadrant)
$x = \frac{6\pi}{6} + \frac{\pi}{6}$	or	$x = \frac{12\pi}{6} - \frac{\pi}{6}$
$\boldsymbol{x = \frac{7\pi}{6}}$	or	$\boldsymbol{x = \frac{11\pi}{6}}$

note:

A graphical check may be made using the 'sine graph':

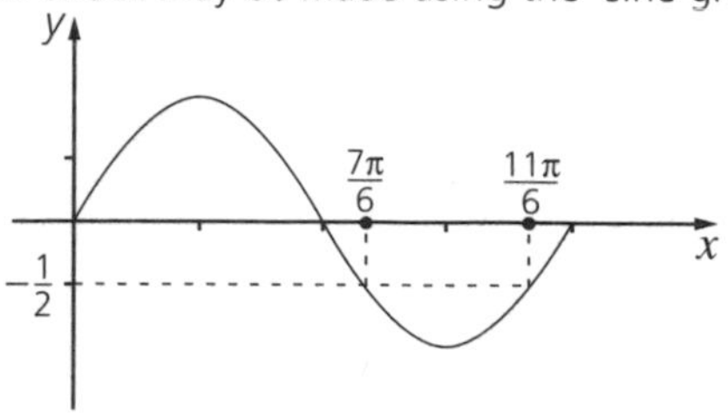

The diagram indicates the two solutions to $\sin x = -\frac{1}{2}$.

example 4.4

Solve $\cos^2 2x = 1$ for $0 \leq x \leq 2\pi$

solution:

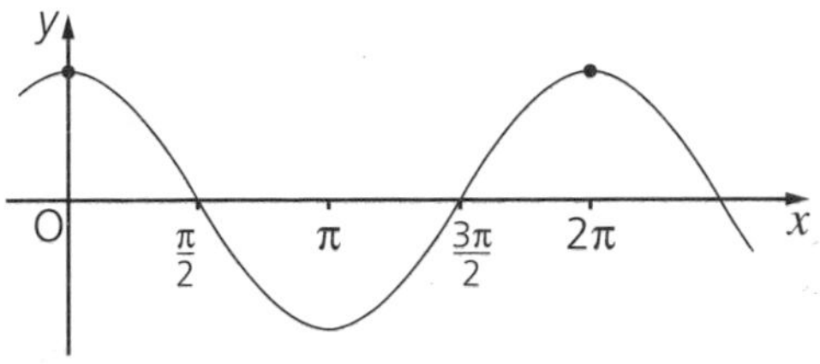

$\cos^2 2x = 1 \Rightarrow \cos 2x = \pm 1$
the cosine graph gives $2x = 0, \pi, 2\pi, 3\pi, 4\pi, \ldots$

So $\mathbf{x = 0, \frac{\pi}{2}, \pi, \frac{3\pi}{2}, 2\pi}$
(only solutions for $0 \leq x \leq 2\pi$)

example 4.5

Solve $3\cos(2x - \frac{\pi}{6}) = 2$ for $0 \leq x < \pi$

solution:
Rearrange to $\cos(2x - \frac{\pi}{6}) = \frac{2}{3}$
So the angle $2x - \frac{\pi}{6}$ is in the 1st or 4th quadrants since cosine is positive in these quadrants.

Set calculator to Radian Mode. Enter $\frac{2}{3}$ and $\boxed{\cos^{-1}}$ giving 0·841 radians as the 1st quadrant angle.

So	$2x - \frac{\pi}{6} = 0{\cdot}841$ (1st quad)	or	$2x - \frac{\pi}{6} = 2\pi - 0{\cdot}841$ (4th quad)
giving	$2x = 0{\cdot}841 + \frac{\pi}{6}$ $= 1{\cdot}364\ldots$	or	$2x = 2\pi - 0{\cdot}841 + \frac{\pi}{6}$ $= 5{\cdot}965\ldots$
so	$\mathbf{x = 0{\cdot}682}$	or	$\mathbf{x = 2{\cdot}983}$ (to 3 dec. places)

Quadratic Trig Equations

$3\cos^2 x + 7\cos x - 6 = 0$ ←— compare —→ $3c^2 + 7c - 6 = 0$

$(3\cos x - 2)(\cos x + 3) = 0$ | $(3c - 2)(c + 3) = 0$

$3\cos x - 2 = 0$ or $\cos x + 3 = 0$

$3\cos x = 2$ | $\cos x = -3$

$\cos x = \frac{2}{3}$ (x is in 1st or 4th quads) etc | (no solutions since $-1 \leq \cos x \leq 1$)

$3c - 2 = 0$ or $c + 3 = 0$

$3c = 2$ | $c = -3$

$c = \frac{2}{3}$

5. Introduction to Differentiation

What is differentiation all about?

It's about finding gradients of graphs.
On the graph $y = f(x)$ let's find the gradient at the point A where $x = a$. First make a small triangle at the point A.

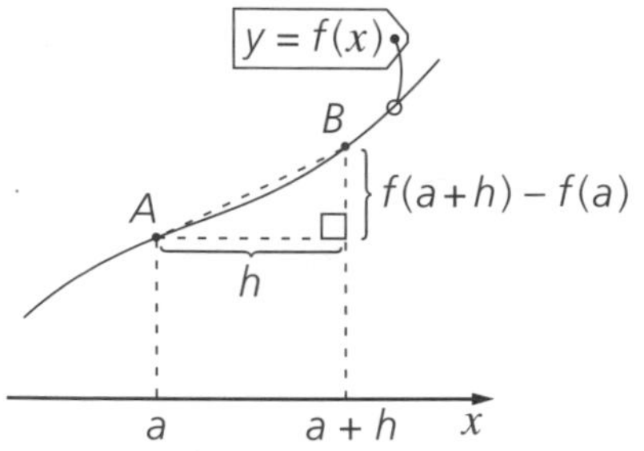

Then calculate the gradient of line AB: $\dfrac{f(a+h)-f(a)}{h}$

Now shrink the triangle:

as $h \xrightarrow{\text{approaches}} 0$ so $\dfrac{f(a+h)-f(a)}{h} \xrightarrow{\text{approaches}}$ gradient at $x = a$

There is a limiting value: $\lim\limits_{h\to 0} \dfrac{f(a+h)-f(a)}{h}$
(The limit as h tends to zero)

If this is done for every point on the graph then this process, which is called **Differentiation**, produces a gradient formula, the **derived** formula f':

$$f'(x) = \lim_{h\to 0} \frac{f(a+h)-f(a)}{h}$$

(Don't worry! You don't need to know how to use this.)

$f(x)$ formula	**differentiate** ⟶	**$f'(x)$** gradient formula

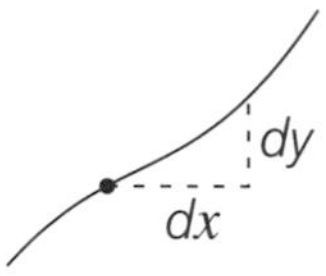

$\dfrac{dy}{dx}$ is also used for the gradient.

Think of it as the 'amazing shrinking triangle trick': when the triangle disappears it miraculously leaves behind the gradient formula:

$$\frac{\text{The disappeared } y}{\text{The disappeared } x} = \frac{dy}{dx}$$

Some Rules

$f(x)$	$f'(x)$
x^n	nx^{n-1}
$g(x) \pm h(x)$	$g'(x) \pm h'(x)$
(Differentiate each term of a sum or difference.)	
$ag(x)$	$ag'(x)$
(When a term is multiplied by a constant then differentiate as normal and multiply the result by the same constant.)	

notes: Special cases

1.

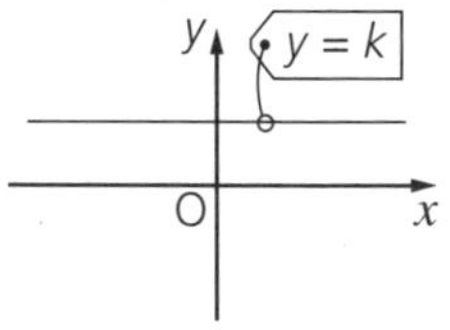

$y = k$
gives $\frac{dy}{dx} = 0$

Differentiating a constant gives zero since the gradient of a constant graph is zero.

2.

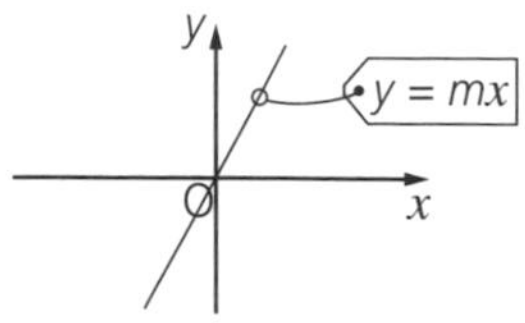

$y = mx$
gives $\frac{dy}{dx} = m$

The gradient of $y = mx$ is m.

example 5.1

Differentiate:

a) $y = 5x^3 - 3x^2$

solution:
Differentiate each term.

$$\frac{dy}{dx} = 5 \times 3x^2 - 3 \times 2x^1$$
$$= \mathbf{15x^2 - 6x}$$

b) $f(x) = \dfrac{2}{\sqrt{x}} - \dfrac{3}{x}$

solution:
First prepare the 'formula' for differentiating by writing it as powers of x.

$$f(x) = \frac{2}{x^{\frac{1}{2}}} - \frac{3}{x^1} = 2x^{-\frac{1}{2}} - 3x^{-1}$$

so $$f'(x) = 2 \times \left(-\tfrac{1}{2}\right)x^{-\frac{3}{2}} - 3 \times (-1)x^{-2}$$
$$= -x^{-\frac{3}{2}} + 3x^{-2}$$
$$= -\frac{\mathbf{1}}{\boldsymbol{x^{\frac{3}{2}}}} + \frac{\mathbf{3}}{\boldsymbol{x^2}}$$

Hints on preparing formulae for differentiating

The aim is to write the formula as a sum or difference of terms like: ax^n

hint 1 Remove root signs

eg $\sqrt{x} = x^{\frac{1}{2}}$ $\quad \frac{1}{\sqrt{x}} = x^{-\frac{1}{2}}$

hint 2 Remove brackets

eg $(2x-1)(x+2) = 2x^2 + 3x - 2$

hint 3 Fractions with a single term on the denominator can be split:

$$\text{eg } \frac{x^3 + x - 1}{x^2} = \frac{x^3}{x^2} + \frac{x}{x^2} - \frac{1}{x^2}$$

$$= x + x^{-1} - x^{-2}$$

(using the Laws of Indices)

Sketching the Gradient Graph

Given the graph $y = f(x)$ how do you sketch the gradient graph $y = f'(x)$?

There are three types of behaviour for the graph $y = f(x)$:

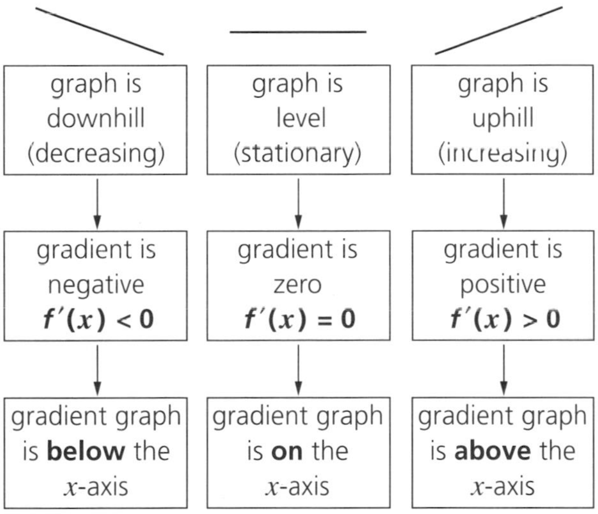

graph is downhill (decreasing)
graph is level (stationary)
graph is uphill (increasing)
gradient is negative
$f'(x) < 0$
gradient is zero
$f'(x) = 0$
gradient is positive
$f'(x) > 0$
gradient graph is **below** the x-axis
gradient graph is **on** the x-axis
gradient graph is **above** the x-axis

It is helpful to divide the graph $y = f(x)$ into sections, each showing one type of behaviour.

example:

Often you will know what shape of graph to expect:

$f(x)$ quadratic (parabola) gives $f'(x)$ linear (straight line)

$f(x)$ cubic (see example) gives $f'(x)$ quadratic (parabola)

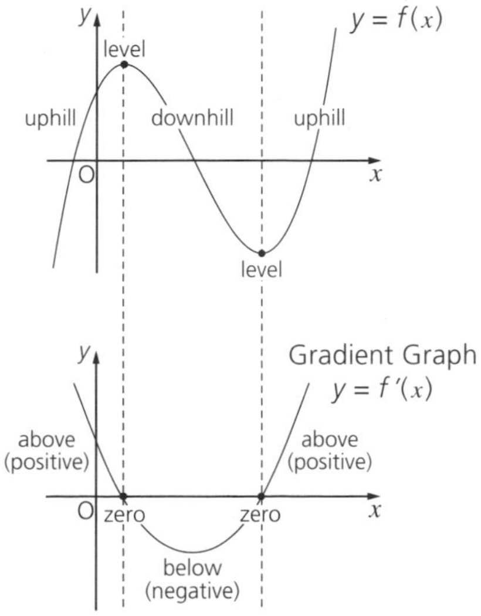

---

example 5.2

Calculate the **exact** value of $f'(9)$ where

$$f(x) = \frac{x - 3x^2}{\sqrt{x}}$$

solution:

$$f(x) = \frac{x}{x^{\frac{1}{2}}} - \frac{3x^2}{x^{\frac{1}{2}}} = x^{\frac{1}{2}} - 3x^{\frac{3}{2}}$$

$$\text{So } f'(x) = \frac{1}{2}x^{-\frac{1}{2}} - \frac{9}{2}x^{\frac{1}{2}} = \frac{1}{2\sqrt{x}} - \frac{9\sqrt{x}}{2}$$

$$\text{giving } f'(9) = \frac{1}{2\sqrt{9}} - \frac{9\sqrt{9}}{2} = \frac{1}{6} - \frac{27}{2}$$

$$= \frac{1}{6} - \frac{81}{6} = -\frac{80}{6} = -\mathbf{\frac{40}{3}}$$

A decimal approximation is not acceptable for the **exact** value.

---

example 5.3

a) Find the gradient of the curve $y = x^3$ at the point P(1, 1).

solution:

$\frac{dy}{dx} = 3x^2$

When $x = 1$

$\frac{dy}{dx} = 3 \times 1^2 = 3$

The required **gradient is 3**.

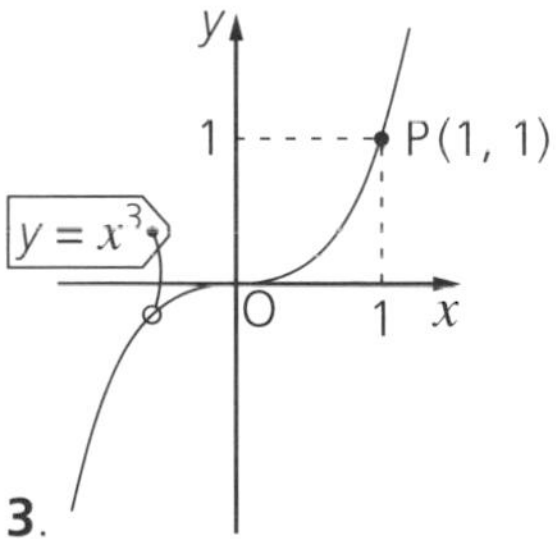

b) Find the points on the curve $y = x^3$ where the gradient is 12.

solution:

You require $\frac{dy}{dx} = 12$ so $3x^2 = 12$, $x^2 = 4$

giving $x = 2$ or -2

The required points are **(2, 8) and (–2, –8)**.

5. Introduction to Differentiation

Tangents to Graphs

The gradient of the tangent to the graph $y = f(x)$ at the point (x, y) is given by

$$\frac{dy}{dx} \text{ or } f'(x)$$

In particular, at the point (a, b) the gradient of the tangent is $f'(a)$.

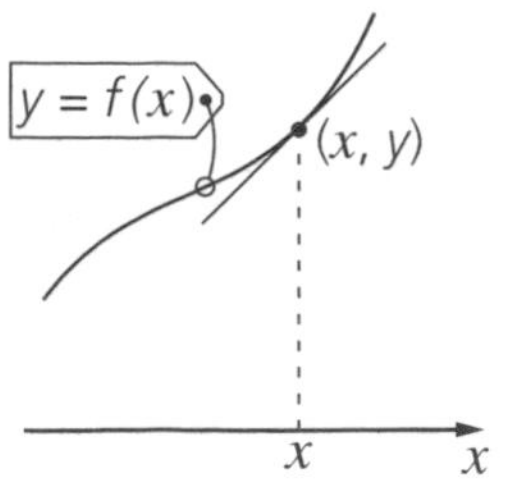

To Find the Equation of a Tangent

At the point (a, b) on the graph $y = f(x)$

step 1 Find $f'(x)$

step 2 Calculate $m = f'(a)$

step 3 Equation is $y - b = m(x - a)$

Stationary Points

Points on a graph $y = f(x)$ where the gradient is zero are called **stationary points**.

$$f'(a) = 0$$

$(a, f(a))$ is a stationary **point**.

$f(a)$ is a stationary **value**.

Here are the different types of stationary points that may appear on a graph:

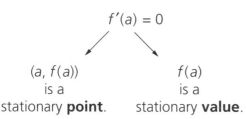

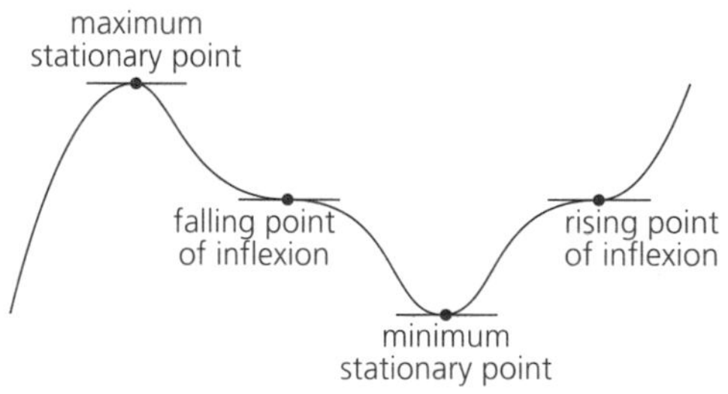

To Find the Stationary Points

On the graph $y = f(x)$

step 1 Find $f'(x)$

step 2 Set $f'(x) = 0$

step 3 Solve $f'(x) = 0$

Each solution $x = a$ gives a stationary point.

step 4 Calculate $y = f(a)$ for each solution $x = a$. $(a, f(a))$ is a stationary point.

example 5.4

Find the equation of the tangent to $y = x^2$ at the point (3, 9)

solution:

First find the gradient of the tangent by differentiating and then replace x by 3.

$y = x^2$ gives $\frac{dy}{dx} = 2x$

when $x = 3$ $\frac{dy}{dx} = 2 \times 3 = 6$

The gradient of the tangent is 6. A point on the tangent is (3, 9) so the equation of the tangent is…

$y - 9 = 6(x - 3)$ ($y - b = m(x - a)$)

$y - 9 = 6x - 18$

$\mathbf{y = 6x - 9}$

example 5.5

Find the stationary points on the graph

$$y = x^4 - 4x^3 + 3$$

solution:

$$y = x^4 - 4x^3 + 3 \text{ gives } \frac{dy}{dx} = 4x^3 - 12x^2$$

To find stationary points, set $\frac{dy}{dx} = 0$

so $4x^3 - 12x^2 = 0$

Now solve: $4x^2(x - 3) = 0$

$x^2 = 0$, $x = 0$ or $x - 3 = 0$, $x = 3$

when $x = 0$ $y = 0^4 - 4 \times 0^3 + 3 = 3$ giving (0, 3)

when $x = 3$ $y = 3^4 - 4 \times 3^3 + 3 = -24$ giving (3, −24)

So there are two stationary points, namely (0, 3) and (3, −24), on this graph.

A Table of Signs

Having identified where the stationary points are, say, at $x = a$ and $x = b$, then:

step 1 Draw a number line and place the x-values, $x = a$ and $x = b$, in order on the number line.

step 2 Underneath draw a two-row table:

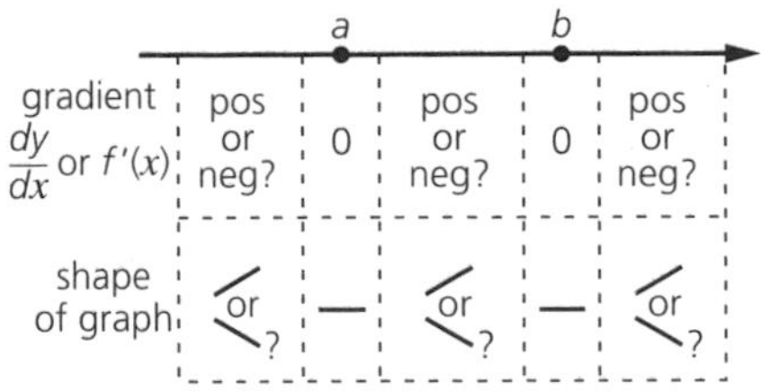

example 5.6

Determine the **nature** of the stationary points from example 5.5.

solution:

$\frac{dy}{dx} = 4x^3 - 12x^2$

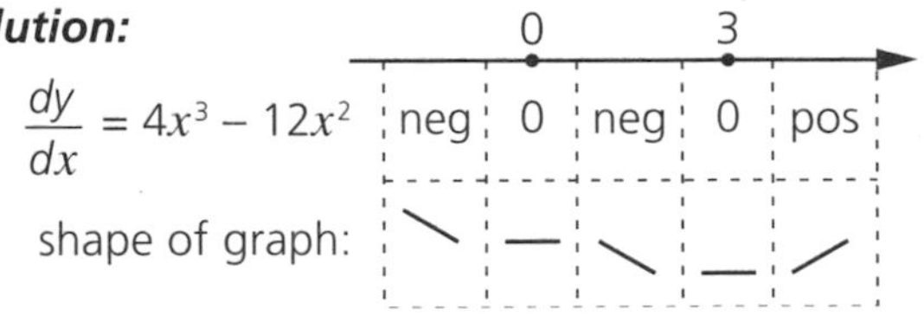

So (0, 3) is a falling point of inflexion and (3, –24) is a minimum stationary point.

Identifying Types of Stationary Points

Use the gradient formula $y = f'(x)$ to find the **sign** of the gradient just to the left and to the right of the stationary point. Here are the results:

A Maximum:

graph is uphill (increasing)	graph is level (stationary)	graph is downhill (decreasing)
gradient is positive	gradient is zero	gradient is negative
$\frac{dy}{dx} > 0$	$\frac{dy}{dx} = 0$	$\frac{dy}{dx} < 0$
+	0	–

A Minimum:

graph is downhill (decreasing)	graph is level (stationary)	graph is uphill (increasing)
gradient is negative	gradient is zero	gradient is positive
$\frac{dy}{dx} < 0$	$\frac{dy}{dx} = 0$	$\frac{dy}{dx} > 0$
–	0	+

Horizontal Points of Inflexion:

Falling:

graph is downhill (decreasing)	graph is level (stationary)	graph is downhill (decreasing)
gradient is negative	gradient is zero	gradient is negative
$\frac{dy}{dx} < 0$	$\frac{dy}{dx} = 0$	$\frac{dy}{dx} < 0$

Rising:

graph is uphill (increasing)	graph is level (stationary)	graph is uphill (increasing)
gradient is positive	gradient is zero	gradient is positive
$\frac{dy}{dx} > 0$	$\frac{dy}{dx} = 0$	$\frac{dy}{dx} > 0$

Hints on Graph Sketching

Example:

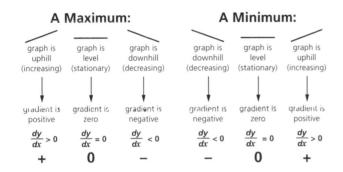

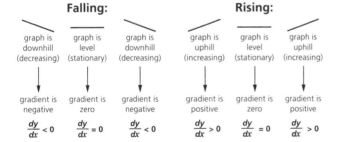

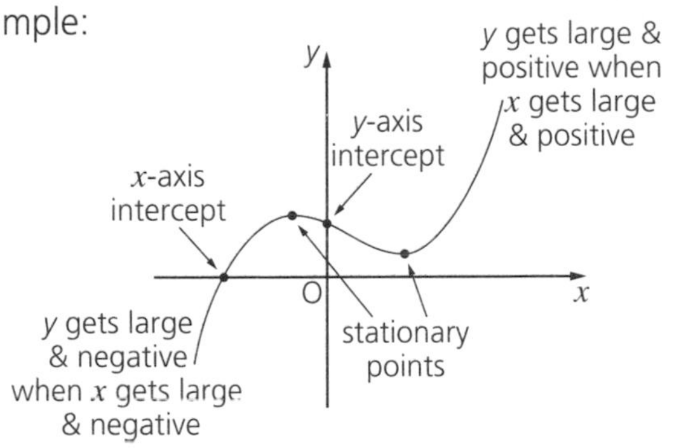

For any graph $y = f(x)$:

hint 1 Find where the graph cuts the axes:
y-axis intercept: set $x = 0$ and find $y = f(0)$
x-axis intercept: set $y = f(x) = 0$ and solve the equation.

hint 2 Find the stationary points and determine their nature.

hint 3 Check the behaviour of y for large positive/negative x values.

Warning
Graphic calculators are excellent for showing graphs but if you are asked to 'show' or 'prove' that a point is a maximum or minimum stationary point then you must use a **table of signs**.

5. Introduction to Differentiation

Greatest and Least Values

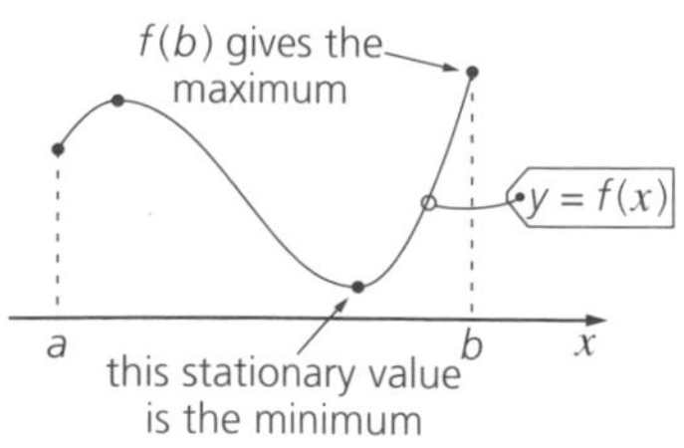

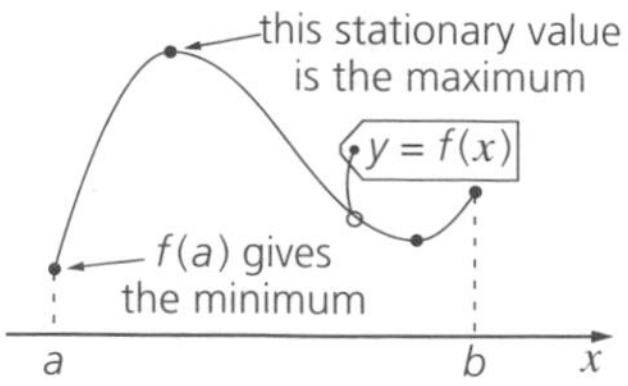

Depending on the shape of the graph, for a given **interval** $a \le x \le b$ (all values of x from a to b), the maximum/minimum value of f will be found at...

the stationary points **or** the end points. ($x = a$ and $x = b$)

example 5.7

Find the maximum and minimum values of $f(x) = x^3 - 3x + 2$ on the interval $-2 \le x \le 3$

solution:

Solving $f'(x) = 3x^2 - 3 = 0$ gives stationary points at $x = 1$ and $x = -1$ with $f(1) = 0$ and $f(-1) = 4$

The values at the end points of the interval are $f(-2) = 0$ and $f(3) = 20$

The maximum value is 20 (when $x = 3$).

The minimum value is 0 (when $x = -2$ and when $x = 1$).

Examples of Rates of Change

A distance/time graph

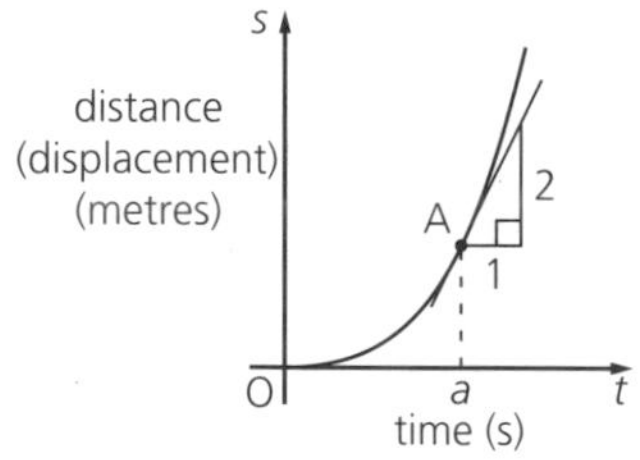

At A, on the graph, the distance is changing at a rate of 2 m each second. In other words, at the time $t = a$, the **speed** is 2 m/s.
The **gradient** of the graph at point A gives the **rate of change** of s with respect to t at the time $t = a$

So $\frac{ds}{dt}$ = speed (velocity).

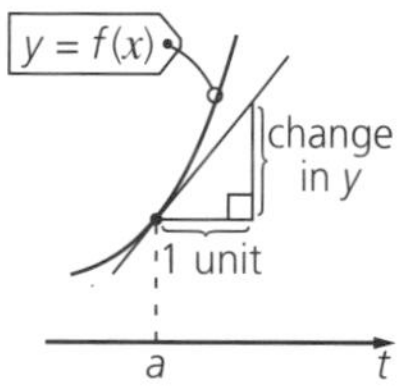

In general:
The **rate of change** of f at $x = a$ is given by $f'(a)$ ($\frac{dy}{dx}$ when $x = a$)
The gradient at a point on the graph measures the rate at which the y-values are changing with respect to x at that point.

A speed/time graph

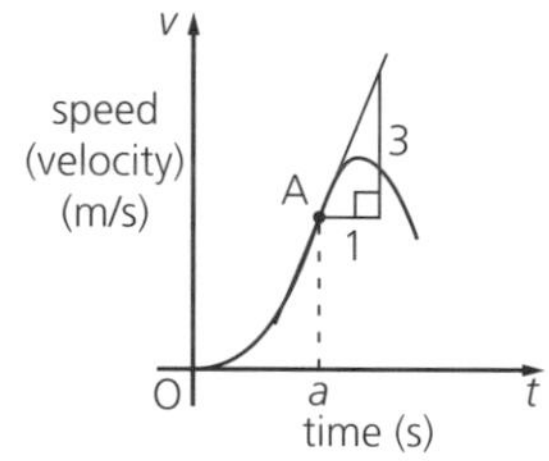

At A, on the graph, the speed is changing at a rate of 3 m/s each second. In other words, at the time $t = a$, the **acceleration** is 3 m/s^2
The **gradient** of the graph at point A gives the **rate of change** of v with respect to t at the time $t = a$

So $\frac{dv}{dt}$ = acceleration.

example 5.8

The displacement, s cm, of a weight on a spring, t seconds after release is given by $s = 50t - 100t^2$. Find its velocity when released and after $\frac{1}{4}$ second.

solution:

$$v = \frac{ds}{dt} = 50 - 200t$$

At time of release $t = 0$ so $v = 50 - 200 \times 0 =$ **50 m/s**

After $\frac{1}{4}$ second $t = \frac{1}{4}$ so $v = 50 - 200 \times \frac{1}{4} =$ **0 m/s**
(it has reached its greatest extent)

example 5.9

The volume, V cm^3, of a spherical balloon with radius r cm is given by $V = \frac{4}{3}\pi r^3$. It is inflated.

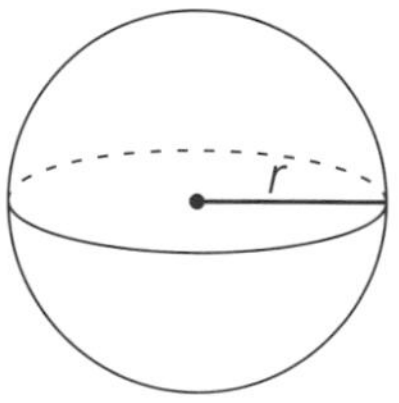

Find the rate of change of V with respect to r when $r = 8$ cm.

solution:

$V = \dfrac{4}{3}\pi r^3$ so $\dfrac{dV}{dr} = 3 \times \dfrac{4}{3}\pi r^2 = 4\pi r^2$ — This is the 'rate of change formula'.

When $r = 8$, $\dfrac{dV}{dr} = 4 \times \pi \times 8^2 \doteqdot 804$ (to 3 sig. figs.).

This means that when the balloon has radius 8 cm and if the rate at which the volume is changing were to remain the same, then for an increase of 1 cm in the radius the volume would increase by 804 cm^3.

Some Notation

For this sequence:

1, 3, 7, 15, 31, ...

You can label the terms:

$u_1, u_2, u_3, u_4, u_5, \ldots u_{n-1}, u_n, u_{n+1}, \ldots$

u_n is the label attached to the nth term of the sequence.

n^{th} term formulae

u_1,	u_2,	u_3,	u_4,	...	u_n
1,	3,	7,	15	...	
$2^1 - 1$,	$2^2 - 1$,	$2^3 - 1$,	$2^4 - 1$	...	$2^n - 1$

So $u_n = 2^n - 1$

This is an nth term formula.

Recurrence Relations

1 → 3 → 7 → 15 ...

(each step: double, add 1)

So $u_1 \to u_2$ (double, add 1) gives $u_2 = 2u_1 + 1$

$u_2 \to u_3$ (double, add 1) gives $u_3 = 2u_2 + 1$

and in general

$u_n \to u_{n+1}$ (double, add 1) gives $u_{n+1} = 2u_n + 1$

This is a **recurrence relation**: it recurs as you build up the sequence.

notes:

1. Knowing the recurrence relation is not enough to build up the sequence. The 1st term, u_1, is required to start the process.
2. Different 1st terms give different sequences using the same recurrence relation.
3. Sometimes u_0 is used for the 1st term, so u_{n-1} is the nth term!

Linear Relations

A recurrence relation of the form:

$u_{n+1} = mu_n + c$ (m and c constants)

is **linear**.

m: This is the **multiplier**. c: This is the **constant**.

example 6.1

Find the 10th term in the sequence with n^{th} term $u_n = 3n^2 - 2$

solution: $u_{10} = 3 \times 10^2 - 2 = \mathbf{298}$

example 6.2

Find a recurrence relation and an nth term formula for the sequence 1, 3, 9, 27, ...

solution:

The 'build-up' rule is 'multiply by 3' so the recurrence relation is

$\mathbf{u_{n+1} = 3u_n}$ with $u_1 = 1$

(where u_n is the nth term)

To find the nth term formula compare the terms with the powers of 3:

u_1	u_2	u_3	u_4	
1	3	9	27	one less each time
3^0	3^1	3^2	3^3	

This gives the formula:

$\mathbf{u_n = 3^{n-1}}$

example 6.3

It is known that the sequence 20, 15, 12·5,... has a recurrence relation $u_{n+1} = au_n + b$.

Calculate a and b.

solution:

Using $u_1 = 20$, $u_2 = 15$ gives $15 = 20a + b$

and using $u_2 = 15$, $u_3 = 12{\cdot}5$ gives $12{\cdot}5 = 15a + b$

Solving simultaneously gives $\mathbf{a = 0{\cdot}5}$ and $\mathbf{b = 5}$

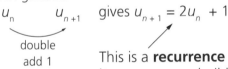

6. Recurrence Relations

Limits

For the recurrence relation

$$u_{n+1} = mu_n + c$$

if $-1 < m < 1$ (the multiplier lies between -1 and 1) then any sequence of values generated by this relation will eventually 'level out' at some limiting value L.

Putting this value L into the recurrence relation will give L again for the next term:

$$L = mL + c$$

so $$L - mL = c$$

$$(1 - m)L = c$$

$$L = \frac{c}{1-m} \quad (-1 < m < 1)$$

This is the **algebraic method** for calculating the limit.

Calculators

On graphic calculators use of the (ANS) key can considerably simplify recurrence relation calculations. For example:

$u_{n+1} = 0{\cdot}5u_n + 5$
with $u_1 = 20$

The calculation is set up as follows:

step 1 Enter 20 then press (EXE)

step 2 Enter 0·5 (ANS) + 5

step 3 Repeatedly press (EXE) to generate the sequence of values.

Warning
Calculating limits this way is a useful check. However marks will not be earned unless the **algebraic method** for calculating the limit is used.

example 6.4

A sequence is defined by the recurrence relation $u_{n+1} = 0{\cdot}7u_n + 14$ with 1st term u_1

a) Explain why this sequence has a limit as n tends to infinity.

solution:
The multiplier 0·7 lies between -1 and 1 and so **a limit exists**.

b) Find the **exact** value of this limit.

solution:
Let the limit be L then $L = 0{\cdot}7L + 14$

so $0{\cdot}3L = 14$ so $L = \dfrac{14}{0{\cdot}3}$

giving $L = \dfrac{140}{3} = \mathbf{46\tfrac{2}{3}}$

example 6.5

During the course of one day an engine uses 15% of its available oil but is then topped-up making a further 2 litres available. With 8 litres initially available, in the long run how much available oil does it have?

solution:
85% of 8 litres + 2 litres = $0{\cdot}85 \times 8 + 2 = 8{\cdot}8$ litres available after 1 day. Let u_n be the number of available litres after n days.

Then $u_{n+1} = 0{\cdot}85u_n + 2$. A limit exists since the multiplier 0·85 lies between -1 and 1.
Let this limit be L.

Then $L = 0{\cdot}85L + 2$ so $0{\cdot}15L = 2$ so $L = \dfrac{2}{0{\cdot}15}$

$= \dfrac{200}{15} = \dfrac{40}{3} = \mathbf{13\tfrac{1}{3}}$ litres available in the long run.

Problems in Context

step 1
To solve the problem you will probably need to do a recurring calculation to produce a sequence of values. Try to calculate the first few values (eg 10 tonnes of pollutant, 1 week later 12·5 tonnes etc).

step 2
If u_n is the nth term in this sequence of values then state clearly what meaning u_n has in the given context (eg u_n is number of tonnes of pollutant after n weeks).

step 3
Describe the recurring calculation using u_{n+1} and u_n (eg $u_{n+1} = 0{\cdot}8u_n + 2$).

step 4
Use this recurrence relation to solve the problem (eg calculate a limit etc).

What is a Polynomial?

A **polynomial** consists of sums and/or differences of terms like:

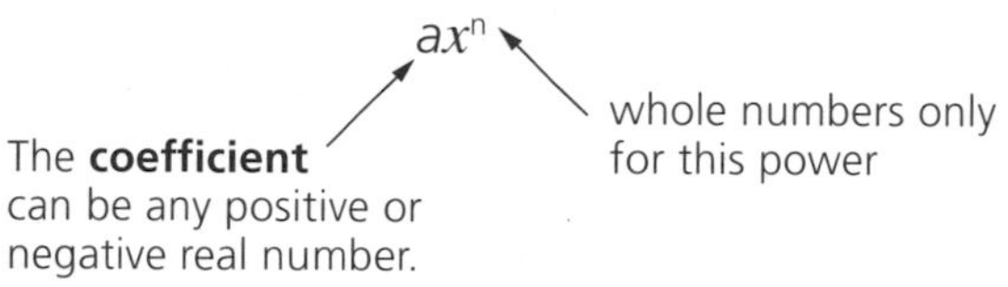
ax^n
The **coefficient** can be any positive or negative real number.
whole numbers only for this power

example:

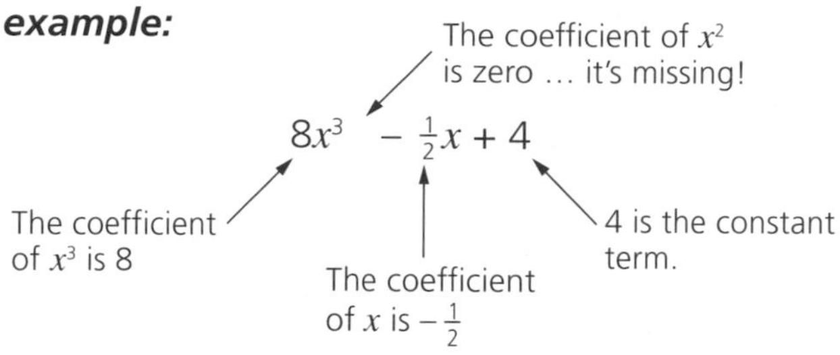
$8x^3 - \frac{1}{2}x + 4$
The coefficient of x^2 is zero … it's missing!
The coefficient of x^3 is 8
The coefficient of x is $-\frac{1}{2}$
4 is the constant term.

The highest power of x is the **degree** of the polynomial (3 in the example above).

example 7.1

Give the degree of these polynomials or state if they are not polynomials:

3 (degree 0) (constant)	$x^{-1} + x^{-2}$ (not a polynomial)	$3x^2$ (degree 2) (Quadratic)
$15 - 2x$ (degree1) (Linear)	$2x^2 - x + 3$ (degree 2) (Quadratic)	
$\sqrt{x}$ (not a polynomial)	$4x^3 + 2x$ (degree 3) (Cubic)	$3x^{\frac{3}{2}}$ (not a polynomial)

The Synthetic Division Scheme

Keep this division in your mind:

Divide 7 by 2: $2 \,\underline{|7}$
$\quad\quad\quad\quad\quad 3$ r 1

so $\quad 7 = 2 \times \underbrace{3}_{\textbf{quotient}} + \underbrace{1}_{\textbf{remainder}}$

Similarly polynomials can be divided by linear expressions. This example shows how:

Divide $f(x) = 2x^3 - 7x^2 + 16$ by $x - 2$

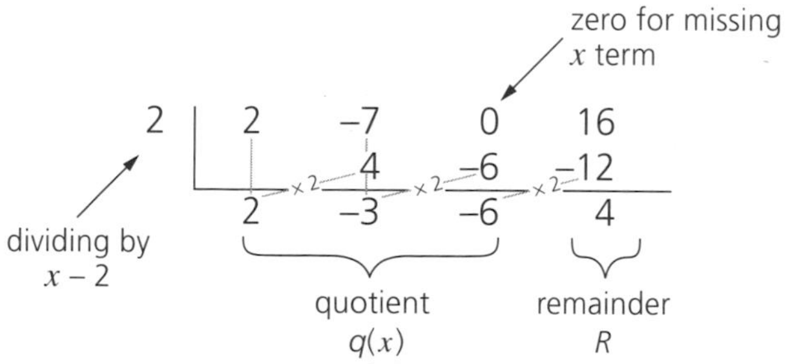
zero for missing
x term
2
2 -7 0 16
4 -6 -12
2 -3 -6 4
×2
dividing by
x – 2
quotient
q(x)
remainder
R

So $f(x) = (x - 2)(2x^2 - 3x - 6) + 4$.
Also notice that $f(2) = 0 \times (2x^2 - 3x - 6) + 4$
so $f(2)$ gives the remainder 4

example 7.2

Let $f(x) = 2x^3 - 3x + 10$

a) Find $f(-3)$

solution:

$$\begin{array}{r|rrrr} -3 & 2 & 0 & -3 & 10 \\ & & -6 & 18 & -45 \\ \hline & 2 & -6 & 15 & -35 \end{array}$$

So $f(-3) = -35$

b) Find the remainder when $f(x)$ is divided by $x - 2$

solution:

$$\begin{array}{r|rrrr} 2 & 2 & 0 & -3 & 10 \\ & & 4 & 8 & 10 \\ \hline & 2 & 4 & 5 & 20 \end{array}$$

So $f(x) = (x - 2)(2x^2 + 4x + 5) + 20$
and the remainder is 20

note: $f(2) = 20$

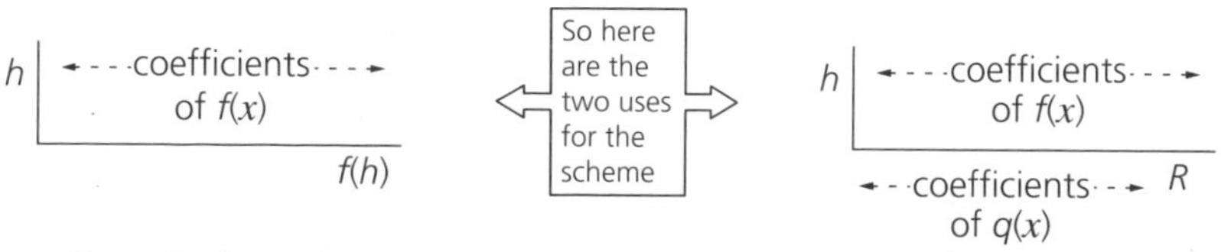
h
coefficients
of f(x)
f(h)
So here
are the
two uses
for the
scheme
h
coefficients
of f(x)
coefficients
of q(x)
R

To calculate the value of $f(h)$.

To calculate the quotient and remainder when $f(x)$ is divided by $x - h$
ie $f(x) = (x - h)q(x) + R$

note: The fact that $R = f(h)$ is called 'The Remainder Theorem'.

Factorising Polynomials

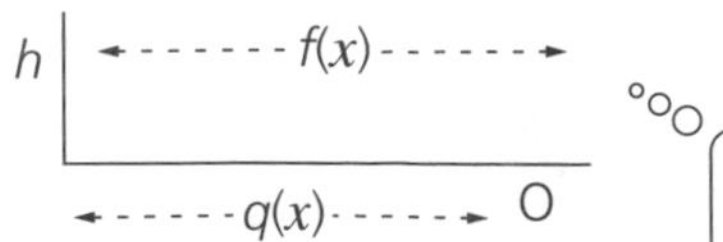

Compare $2\underline{|6}$
$\quad 3 \text{ r } 0$
$6 = 2 \times 3$
2 is a **factor** of 6

$f(x) = (x - h)q(x)$
$(x - h)$ is a **factor** of $f(x)$

Remainder is zero. $\Longleftrightarrow$ $x - h$ is a factor.

note: This result is called 'The Factor Theorem'.

Solving Polynomial Equations

The general method is:

$$f(x) = 0$$

$$(1^{\text{st}} \text{ factor}) \times (2^{\text{nd}} \text{ factor}) \times (3^{\text{rd}} \text{ factor})\ldots = 0$$

$$\begin{pmatrix}1^{\text{st}}\\ \text{factor}\end{pmatrix} = 0 \text{ or } \begin{pmatrix}2^{\text{nd}}\\ \text{factor}\end{pmatrix} = 0 \text{ or } \begin{pmatrix}3^{\text{rd}}\\ \text{factor}\end{pmatrix} = 0$$

Use the Synthetic Division Scheme to start the factorisation process, then factorise any quadratics as normal.

example 7.3

a) Factorise $f(x) = x^3 + 2x^2 - 5x - 6$

solution: Divide $f(x)$ by $x - 1$:

1	1	2	−5	−6
		1	3	−2
	1	3	−2	−8

remainder is not zero so $x - 1$ is not a factor

Now let's try $x + 1$ as a candidate:

−1	1	2	−5	−6
		−1	−1	6
	1	1	−6	0

remainder is zero so $x + 1$ is a factor

So $f(x) = (x + 1)(x^2 + x - 6)$ ← quadratic factorising
$= (x + 1)(x - 2)(x + 3)$

b) and hence solve $f(x) = 0$

solution:
The equation becomes $(x + 1)(x - 2)(x + 3) = 0$

So $x + 1 = 0$ or $x - 2 = 0$ or $x + 3 = 0$
$x = -1$ $\quad x = 2$ $\quad x = -3$

The roots are **−3, −1 and 2**

Roots, Factor and Graphs

If $x - h$ is a factor of $f(x)$ then h is a root of $f(x) = 0$ and the graph $y = f(x)$ cuts the x-axis at $(h, 0)$.

example: Let $f(x) = x^3 + 2x^2 - 5x - 6$
$f(x) = (x + 3)(x + 1)(x - 2)$

The roots of $f(x) = 0$ are: −3 −1 2

The graph $y = f(x)$

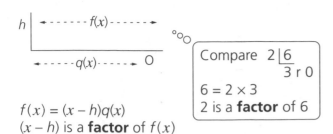

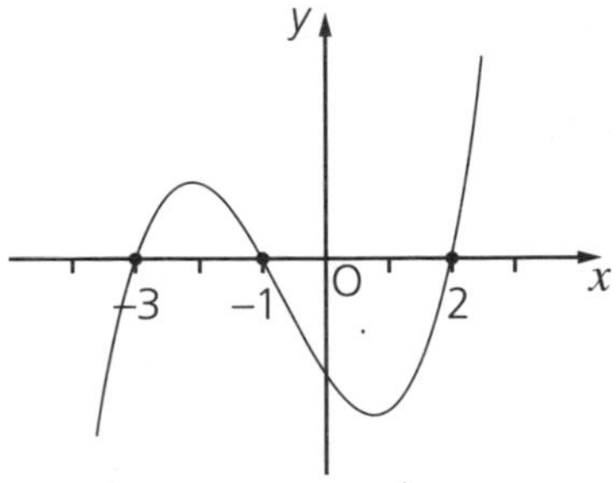

The roots of $f(x) = 0$ are given by the x-axis intercepts.

example 7.4

Show that $\frac{1}{2}$ is a root of $12x^3 - 28x^2 - 9x + 10 = 0$ and find the other two roots.

solution:
Let $f(x) = 12x^3 - 28x^2 - 9x + 10$
The 'Division Scheme' gives:

$\frac{1}{2}$	12	−28	−9	10
		6	−11	−10
	12	−22	−20	0

Since $f(\frac{1}{2}) = 0$ then $\frac{1}{2}$ is a root.
Using the table above…
$f(x) = (x - \frac{1}{2})(12x^2 - 22x - 20)$
$= (x - \frac{1}{2}) \times 2(6x^2 - 11x - 10)$
$= (2x - 1)(6x^2 - 11x - 10)$
so
$f(x) = (2x - 1)(3x + 2)(2x - 5)$
and so $f(x) = 0$ gives
$2x - 1 = 0$ or $3x + 2 = 0$ or $2x - 5 = 0$
$\boldsymbol{x = \frac{1}{2}}$ $\quad \boldsymbol{x = -\frac{2}{3}}$ $\quad \boldsymbol{x = \frac{5}{2}}$

Roots of a Quadratic Equation

If a quadratic equation cannot be solved by factorising then you can use **The Quadratic Formula**. This formula solves **any** quadratic equation:

ax^2	+	bx	+	$c = 0$
↑ the number of x^2s ↓ a		↑ the number of xs ↓ b		↑ the constant ↓ c

$$ax^2 + bx + c = 0$$

$$x = \frac{-b + \sqrt{b^2 - 4ac}}{2a} \qquad x = \frac{-b - \sqrt{b^2 - 4ac}}{2a}$$

There appear to be two **roots** or **solutions** but this may not be true. It depends on the number $b^2 - 4ac$ that appears under the square root sign. This number is called **The Discriminant**.

The Discriminant

The graph of $y = ax^2 + bx + c$ meets the x-axis at 2 points.	The graph of $y = ax^2 + bx + c$ meets the x-axis at 1 point.	The graph of $y = ax^2 + bx + c$ does not meet the x-axis
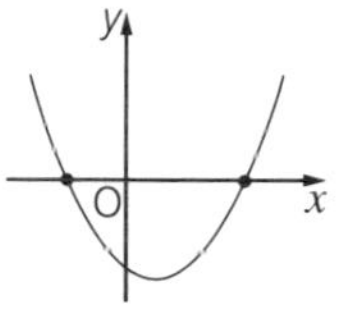	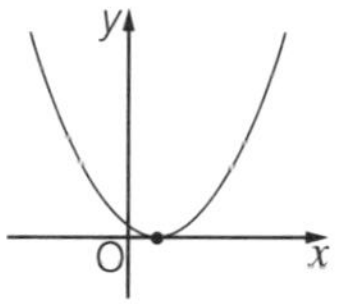	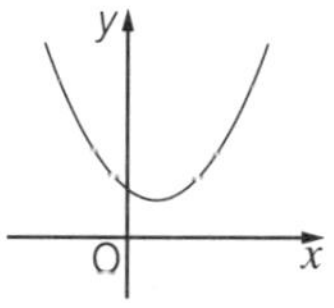
$ax^2 + bx + c = 0$ has **2 distinct roots**	$ax^2 + bx + c = 0$ has **only 1 root** (equal roots)	$ax^2 + bx + c = 0$ has **no real roots**
$b^2 - 4ac > 0$ **discriminant is positive**	$b^2 - 4ac = 0$ **discriminant is zero**	$b^2 - 4ac < 0$ **discriminant is negative**

Calculating the discriminant allows you to determine the **nature** of the roots:

$b^2 - 4ac > 0$ —discriminant positive→ two distinct roots

$b^2 - 4ac = 0$ —discriminant zero→ one root or two equal roots

$b^2 - 4ac < 0$ —discriminant negative→ no real roots

Tangency

The discriminant can be used to show that lines are tangents to curves:

Parabolas 

$y = ax^2 + bx + c$
$y = mx + d$
} For points of intersection replace y by $mx + d$ in the quadratic equation.

Circles 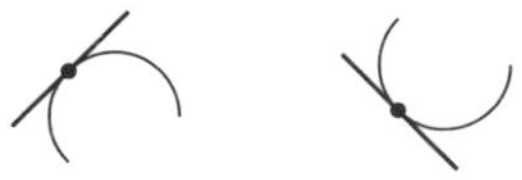

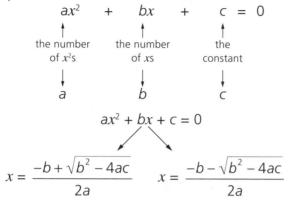

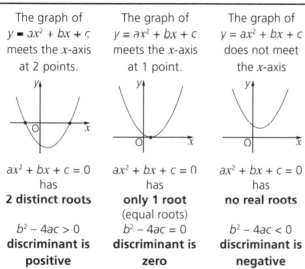

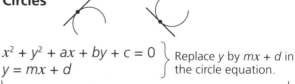

$x^2 + y^2 + ax + by + c = 0$
$y = mx + d$
} Replace y by $mx + d$ in the circle equation.

→ a quadratic equation ←

Calculate the discriminant of this equation. If it is **zero** then there is only **one solution**. This means **one point of intersection** and so the line is **a tangent** to the curve.

example 8.1

Determine the nature of the roots of these equations:

a) $x^2 - 4x + 3 = 0$

b) $x^2 - 4x + 4 = 0$

c) $x^2 - 4x + 5 = 0$

solution:

In each case compare the equation with $ax^2 + bx + c = 0$

a) $a = 1, b = -4, c = 3$
$b^2 - 4ac = (-4)^2 - 4 \times 1 \times 3 = 4$
Discriminant is positive so there are **two distinct roots**.

b) $a = 1, b = -4, c = 4$
$b^2 - 4ac = (-4)^2 - 4 \times 1 \times 4 = 0$
Discriminant is zero so there is **one root** (or there are **equal roots**).

c) $a = 1, b = -4, c = 5$
$b^2 - 4ac = (-4)^2 - 4 \times 1 \times 5 = -4$
Discriminant is negative so there are **no real roots**.

example 8.2

Show that $y = 4x - 2$ is a tangent to the parabola $y = x^2 + 2$

solution:
To find the points of intersection solve:

$$\left.\begin{array}{l} y = x^2 + 2 \\ y = 4x - 2 \end{array}\right\} \text{ so } \begin{array}{l} x^2 + 2 = 4x - 2 \\ x^2 - 4x + 4 = 0 \end{array}$$

Discriminant $= (-4)^2 - 4 \times 1 \times 4 = 0$
so there is one solution and hence one point of intersection. **The line $y = 4x - 2$ is a tangent.**

example 8.3

Show that $y = 2x - 10$ is a tangent to the circle $x^2 + y^2 - 4x + 2y = 0$

solution:
To find the points of intersection solve:

$$\left.\begin{array}{l} x^2 + y^2 - 4x + 2y = 0 \\ y = 2x - 10 \end{array}\right\} \text{Substitute } 2x - 10 \text{ for } y \text{ in the circle equation:}$$

So
$$x^2 + (2x - 10)^2 - 4x + 2(2x - 10) = 0$$
$$x^2 + 4x^2 - 40x + 100 - 4x + 4x - 20 = 0$$
$$5x^2 - 40x + 80 = 0$$
Discriminant $= (-40)^2 - 4 \times 5 \times 80 = 0$

There is one solution, one point of intersection and so **the line $y = 2x - 10$ is a tangent to the circle.**

Imposing Conditions

It may be necessary to impose conditions on the nature of the roots of a quadratic equation. This can be done by applying restrictions to the discriminant. Here's how:

Condition on roots		Restriction on discriminant
Real ('one or two')	$\Longrightarrow$	Positive or zero ($b^2 - 4ac \geq 0$)
Equal ('one')	$\Longrightarrow$	Zero ($b^2 - 4ac = 0$)
Non-real ('none')	$\Longrightarrow$	Negative ($b^2 - 4ac < 0$)

example 8.4

For what values of p does $x^2 - 2x + p = 0$ have real roots?

solution:
Compare $x^2 - 2x + p = 0$
with $ax^2 + bx + c = 0$

This gives $a = 1$, $b = -2$ and $c = p$
Discriminant $= b^2 - 4ac$
$= (-2)^2 - 4 \times 1 \times p$
$= 4 - 4p$
The condition 'real roots' requires the discriminant to be restricted to positive values or zero.
So $4 - 4p \geq 0$ giving $-4p \geq -4$ so $\boldsymbol{p \leq 1}$

example 8.5

Find values of k so that $\dfrac{2(3x+1)}{3x^2+1} = k$ has two equal roots.

solution:
Rearrange the equation...
$6x + 2 = 3kx^2 + k$ giving $3kx^2 - 6x + k - 2 = 0$
and comparing this quadratic equation with $ax^2 + bx + c = 0$ gives $a = 3k$, $b = -6$, $c = k - 2$
Discriminant $= b^2 - 4ac = (-6)^2 - 4 \times 3k(k - 2)$
$= 36 - 12k^2 + 24k$
$= 36 + 24k - 12k^2$
The condition 'equal roots' gives the restriction 'discriminant = 0'.
So $36 + 24k - 12k^2 = 0$ giving $12(3 + 2k - k^2) = 0$
so $12(3 - k)(1 + k) = 0$
This gives two possible values for k namely $\boldsymbol{k = 3}$ **or** $\boldsymbol{k = -1}$

Solving Quadratic Inequalities

If $f(x)$ is any quadratic expression like $ax^2 + bx + c$ then to solve quadratic inequalities like

$f(x) > 0$ or $f(x) < 0$

follow these steps:

step 1 Solve the corresponding quadratic equation $f(x) = 0$ to find the x-axis intercepts for the graph $y = f(x)$.

step 2 Sketch the graph $y = f(x)$ clearly showing the x-axis intercepts.

step 3 Write down the solution using the sketch of the graph $y = f(x)$. Examples are given in this table:

Inequality:	What to look for:	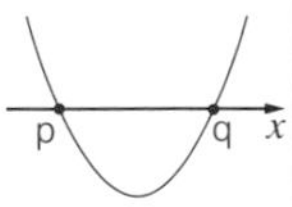 For this graph the solution is:	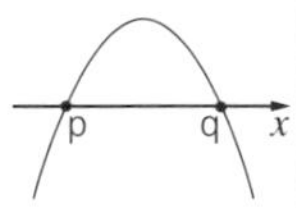 For this graph the solution is:
$ax^2 + bx + c > 0$	Where is the graph **above** the x-axis?	$x < p$ or $x > q$	$p < x < q$
$ax^2 + bx + c < 0$	Where is the graph **below** the x-axis?	$p < x < q$	$x < p$ or $x > q$

note:
If the inequality uses the signs ≤ or ≥ then so will the solution.

example 8.6

Find the real values of x satisfying $2x^2 + x - 1 > 0$

solution:

First solve $\quad 2x^2 + x - 1 = 0$

So $\quad (2x - 1)(x + 1) = 0$

$2x - 1 = 0 \quad$ or $\quad x + 1 = 0$

$x = \frac{1}{2} \qquad\qquad x = -1$

Sketch of $y = 2x^2 + x - 1$

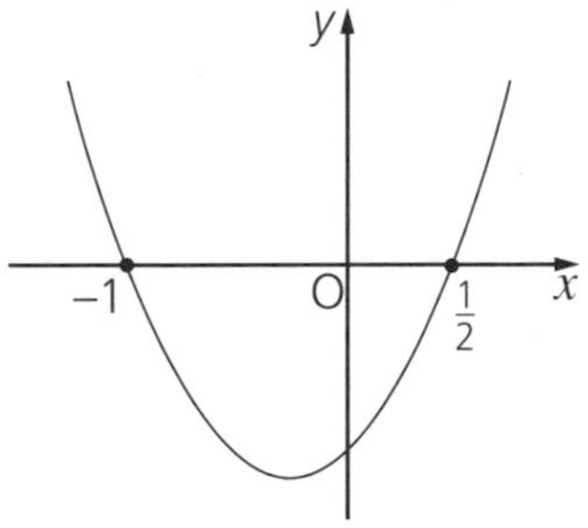

Required solution is $\mathbf{x < -1}$ **or** $\mathbf{x > \frac{1}{2}}$

(graph is **above** x-axis for these values).

Given Roots

It is possible to 'design' a quadratic equation that has two particular roots.

If the roots are $\boldsymbol{x = a}$ and $\boldsymbol{x = b}$

then $\mathbf{(x - a)(x - b) = 0}$ is one such equation.

example 8.7

Find a quadratic equation that has roots $\frac{1}{3}$ and -2

solution:

The required equation is

$$(x - \tfrac{1}{3})(x + 2) = 0$$

This gives $\quad x^2 + 2x - \frac{1}{3}x - \frac{2}{3} = 0$

$$3x^2 + 6x - x - 2 = 0$$

$$\mathbf{3x^2 + 5x - 2 = 0}$$

Finding Approximate Roots

The graph is below the x-axis at $x = a$ and above the x-axis at $x = b$. If the graph is a continuous curve then it must cross the x-axis somewhere between a and b, at $x = \alpha$ say:

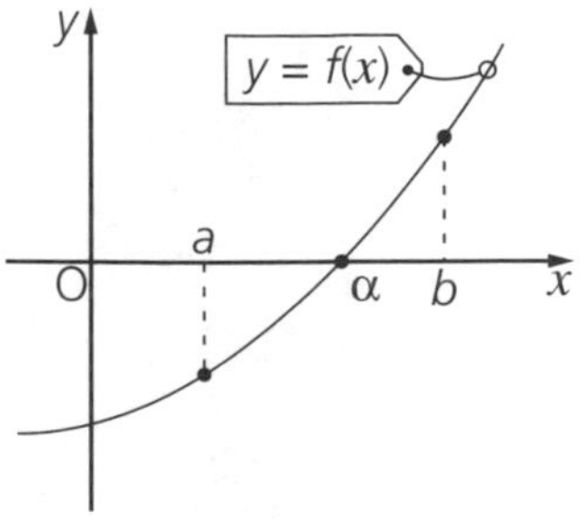

$f(a) < 0$ and $f(b) > 0$	$\Longrightarrow$	**$f(\alpha) = 0$ for some value α with $a < \alpha < b$**

ie $f(x) = 0$ has a root between a and b.

example 8.8

a) Show that $x^3 - 3x + 1 = 0$ has a root between 1 and 2.

solution:
Let $f(x) = x^3 - 3x + 1$

then $f(1) = -1$ so $f(1) < 0$
and $f(2) = 3$ so $f(2) > 0$

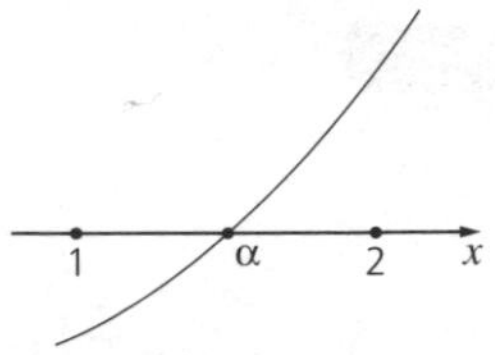

Hence there is a root, α say, with $1 < \alpha < 2$.

b) Find this root, correct to 2 decimal places.

solution:
So far you know $1 < \alpha < 2$.
Testing for more accurate values gives:

$$\left.\begin{array}{l} f(1{\cdot}5) = -0{\cdot}125 < 0 \\ f(1{\cdot}6) = 0{\cdot}296 > 0 \end{array}\right\} \text{ so } 1{\cdot}5 < \alpha < 1{\cdot}6$$

$$\left.\begin{array}{l} f(1{\cdot}53) = -0{\cdot}008 < 0 \\ f(1{\cdot}54) = 0{\cdot}032 > 0 \end{array}\right\} \text{ so } 1{\cdot}53 < \alpha < 1{\cdot}54$$

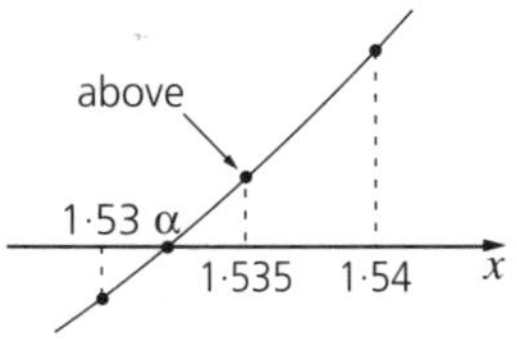

and since $f(1{\cdot}535) = 0{\cdot}012 > 0$
$\alpha \doteqdot 1{\cdot}53$ to 2 decimal places.

Integration

Integration reverses the process of Differentiation:

$$y = f(x) \quad\quad\quad y = f(x) + C$$

$\Downarrow$ differentiation $\quad\quad\quad \Uparrow$ integration

$$\frac{dy}{dx} = f'(x) \quad\quad\quad \frac{dy}{dx} = f'(x)$$

So $\int f'(x)\,dx = f(x) + C$

or $\int g(x)\,dx = G(x) + C$

where $G'(x) = g(x)$

C is called the **Constant of Integration**.

Hints on Preparing Formulae for Integrating

These are the same as for Differentiating (see page 19).

Some Rules

$f(x)$	$\int f(x)\,dx$
x^n	$\frac{x^{n+1}}{n+1} + C \quad (n \neq -1)$
$g(x) \pm h(x)$	$\int g(x)\,dx \pm \int h(x)\,dx$
(Integrate each term of a sum or difference.)	
$ag(x)$	$a\int g(x)\,dx$
(When a term is multiplied by a constant then integrate as normal and multiply the result by the same constant.)	

notes: Special cases

1. Integrating a constant: $\int k\,dx = kx + C$

2. $\int \frac{1}{x}\,dx = \int x^{-1}\,dx$.

This integral does not follow the rule above. You do not need to know how to integrate x^{-1}.

3. A formula may involve a variable other than x, for example $f(t)$, and this may still be integrated:

$\int f(t)\,dt$ (the integral with respect to t).

Differential Equations

$\frac{dy}{dx} = f(x)$ is a **differential equation**.

It has general solution $y = \int f(x)\,dx$

or $y = F(x) + C$ where $F'(x) = f(x)$

note:

$\int f(x)\,dx$ is read 'the integral of $f(x)$ with respect to x' and is called an **Indefinite Integral**.

example 9.1

$\frac{dy}{dx} = 3x^2 - \frac{1}{x^2}$ Find y.

solution:

$$y = \int (3x^2 - x^{-2})\,dx$$

$$= \frac{3x^3}{3} - \frac{x^{-1}}{(-1)} + C$$

$$= \mathbf{x^3 + \frac{1}{x} + C}$$

example 9.2

Find $\int \left(\sqrt{x} - \frac{3}{\sqrt{x}}\right) dx$

solution:

First 'prepare' for integrating.

$$\int \left(x^{\frac{1}{2}} - \frac{3}{x^{\frac{1}{2}}}\right) dx = \int \left(x^{\frac{1}{2}} - 3x^{-\frac{1}{2}}\right) dx$$

$$= \frac{x^{\frac{3}{2}}}{\frac{3}{2}} - \frac{3x^{\frac{1}{2}}}{\frac{1}{2}} + C \quad \text{(Now double top and bottom of fractions.)}$$

$$= \mathbf{\frac{2x^{\frac{3}{2}}}{3} - 6x^{\frac{1}{2}} + C}$$

Definite Integrals

$\int_a^b f(x)\,dx$ is called a **Definite Integral**.

a is the **lower limit** and b is the **upper limit** of the integral. This kind of integral has a particular value. Here are the steps to find this value:

step 1 Integrate $f(x)$ as normal to get $F(x)$ but leave out the constant of integration.

step 2 Calculate $F(b)$ using the upper limit $x = b$.

step 3 Calculate $F(a)$ using the lower limit $x = a$.

step 4 Calculate $F(b) - F(a)$. This is the required value.

So $\int_a^b f(x)\,dx = \left[F(x)\right]_a^b = F(b) - F(a)$

where $F'(x) = f(x)$

The Area Under a Curve

above the x-axis

The shaded area is given by the integral

$\int_a^b f(x)\,dx$

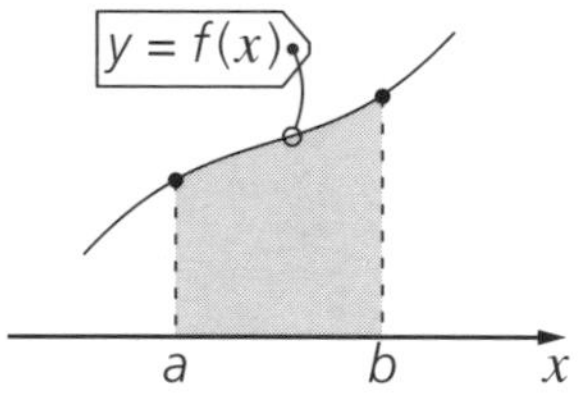

below the x-axis

Calculate $\int_a^b f(x)\,dx$

then change its value from negative to positive so $-\int_a^b f(x)\,dx$ gives the shaded area.

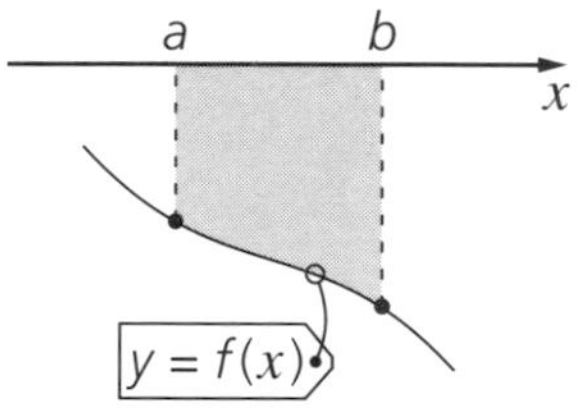

a mixture above and below the x-axis

Add the two separate areas for total shaded area.

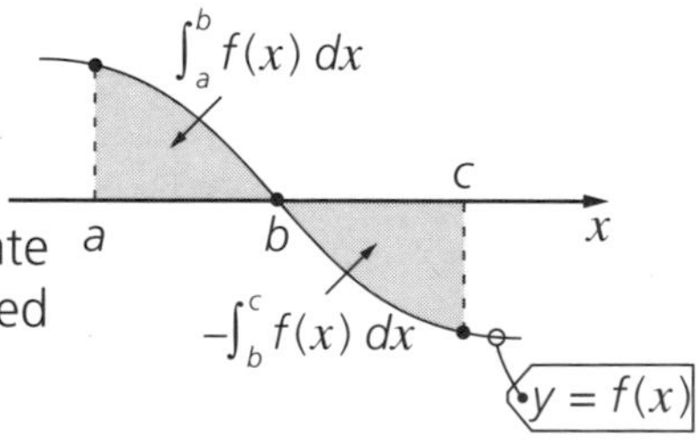

special cases

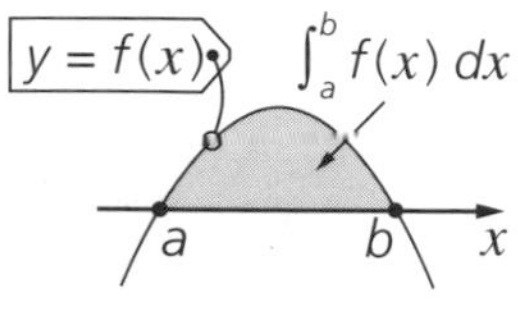

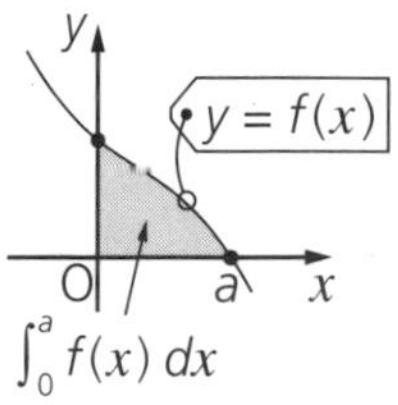

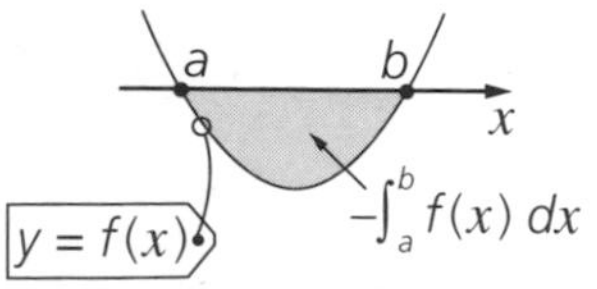

example 9.3

Evaluate $\int_{-1}^{2} 3x^2\,dx$

solution:

$$\int_{-1}^{2} 3x^2\,dx = \left[\frac{3x^3}{3}\right]_{-1}^{2} = \left[x^3\right]_{-1}^{2}$$

$$= 2^3 - (-1)^3 = 8 + 1 = \mathbf{9}$$

example 9.4

Find the **exact** value of $\int_1^3 \left(\frac{3}{\sqrt{x}} - x\right) dx$

solution:

$$\int_1^3 (3x^{-\frac{1}{2}} - x)\,dx = \left[\frac{3x^{\frac{1}{2}}}{\frac{1}{2}} - \frac{x^2}{2}\right]_1^3 = \left[6x^{\frac{1}{2}} - \frac{x^2}{2}\right]_1^3$$

$$= \left[6\sqrt{x} - \frac{x^2}{2}\right]_1^3$$

$$= \left(6\sqrt{3} - \frac{3^2}{2}\right) - \left(6\sqrt{1} - \frac{1^2}{2}\right)$$

$$= 6\sqrt{3} - \frac{9}{2} - 6 + \frac{1}{2}$$

$$= \mathbf{6\sqrt{3} - 10}$$

(Do not give a decimal approximation when an exact value is required.)

example 9.5

Find the area enclosed by $y = x^2 + x - 2$ and the x-axis.

sketch of $y = x^2 + x - 2$

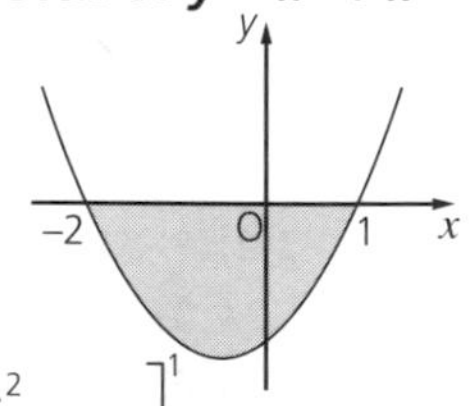

solution:

$y = (x + 2)(x - 1) = 0$

gives $x = -2$ or $x = 1$

First calculate

$$\int_{-2}^{1} \left(x^2 + x - 2\right) dx = \left[\frac{x^3}{3} + \frac{x^2}{2} - 2x\right]_{-2}^{1}$$

$$= \left(\frac{1^3}{3} + \frac{1^2}{2} - 2 \times 1\right) - \left(\frac{(-2)^3}{3} + \frac{(-2)^2}{2} - 2 \times (-2)\right)$$

$$= \frac{1}{3} + \frac{1}{2} - 2 - \left(-\frac{8}{3} + 2 + 4\right) = -\frac{9}{2} = -4\tfrac{1}{2}$$

Since the area is below the x-axis, to get the area change this value from negative to positive.

So required area is $\mathbf{4\frac{1}{2}}$ **unit²**.

note:

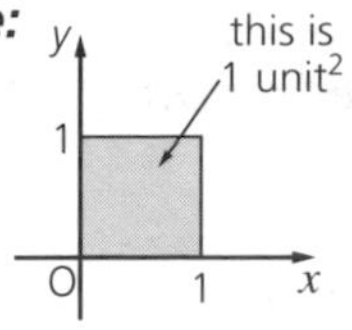

The Area Between Curves

The area of the shaded region enclosed between the two curves is given by

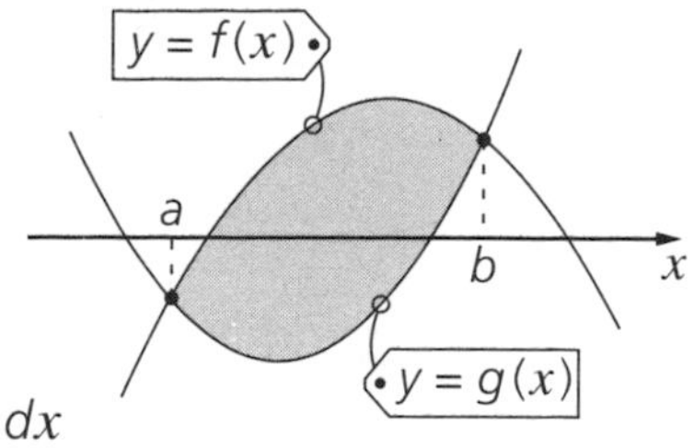

$$\int_a^b f(x) - g(x)\,dx$$

top curve ↗ (f(x)) bottom curve ↖ (g(x))

$x = a$ and $x = b$ are where the curves intersect.

notes:

1. Simplify $f(x) - g(x)$ **first** before integrating… it's usually easier!
2. This result holds wherever the region is relative to the x-axis… above or below or even crossing the x-axis… use the same result.

example 9.6

Find the area of the region enclosed by the line $y = x + 1$ and the parabola $y = 10 + 7x - 3x^2$

solution:

Displaying the graphs on a graphic calculator gives:

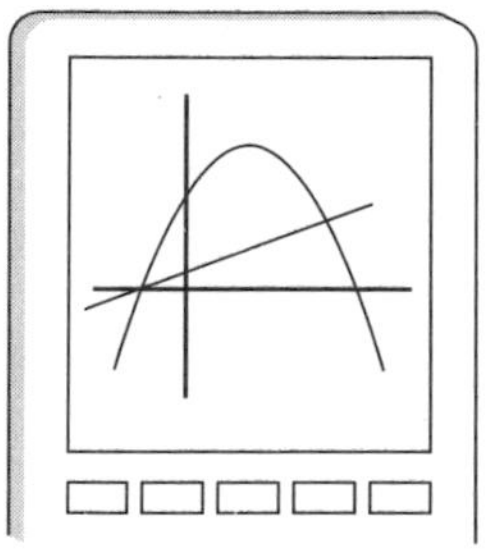

First you must find the two points of intersection of the line and parabola.

Solve:

$y = x + 1$
$y = 10 + 7x - 3x^2$ } So

$x + 1 = 10 + 7x - 3x^2$
$3x^2 - 6x - 9 = 0$
$3(x + 1)(x - 3) = 0$
$x = -1$ or $x = 3$

Sketch of the two graphs:

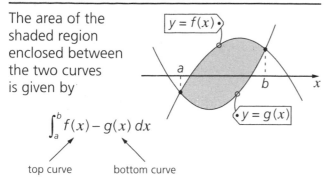

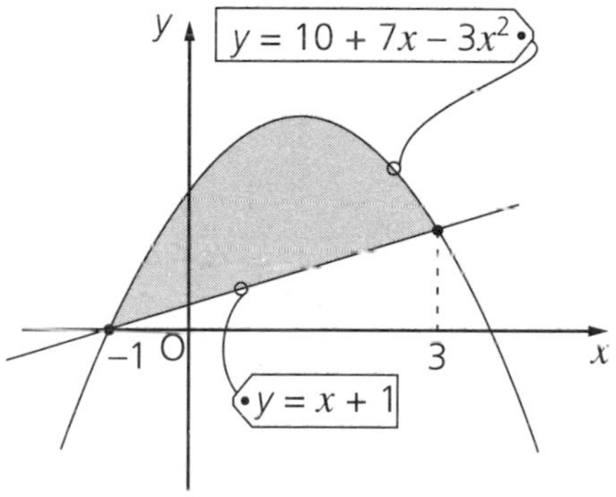

Shaded area

top graph   bottom graph

$$= \int_{-1}^{3} (10 + 7x - 3x^2) - (x + 1)\,dx$$

$$= \int_{-1}^{3} (10 + 7x - 3x^2 - x - 1)\,dx$$

$$= \int_{-1}^{3} (9 + 6x - 3x^2)\,dx$$

$$= \left[9x + \frac{6x^2}{2} - \frac{3x^3}{3}\right]_{-1}^{3}$$

$$= \left[9x + 3x^2 - x^3\right]_{-1}^{3}$$

$= (9 \times 3 + 3 \times 3^2 - 3^3) - (9 \times (-1) + 3 \times (-1)^2 - (-1)^3)$

$= 27 + 27 - 27 + 9 - 3 - 1 =$ **32 unit²**

Examples of Graphs Related to $y = \sin x$

$y = \sin(x + \frac{\pi}{3})$

'shifts' $\frac{\pi}{3}$ to the left
amplitude and period unchanged

$y = 2\sin x$

'stretched'

amplitude is 2
period unchanged

$y = \sin(x - \frac{\pi}{3})$

'shifts' $\frac{\pi}{3}$ to the right
amplitude and period unchanged

$y = \frac{1}{2}\sin x$

'squashed'

amplitude is $\frac{1}{2}$
period unchanged

The **amplitude** is half the difference between the maximum and minimum values on the graph.

The **period** is the 'length' of 1 cycle measured in units along the x-axis.

$y = \sin x$

amplitude

period is 2π, the length of one cycle

$y = -\sin x$

'flipped' in x-axis

amplitude and period unchanged

$y = \sin x - \frac{1}{2}$

'shifts' down by $\frac{1}{2}$

amplitude and period unchanged

$y = \sin 2x$

'squashed'

period is halved
amplitude unchanged

$y = \sin x + \frac{1}{2}$

'shifts' up by $\frac{1}{2}$

amplitude and period unchanged

$y = \sin \frac{1}{2}x$

'stretched'

period is doubled
amplitude unchanged

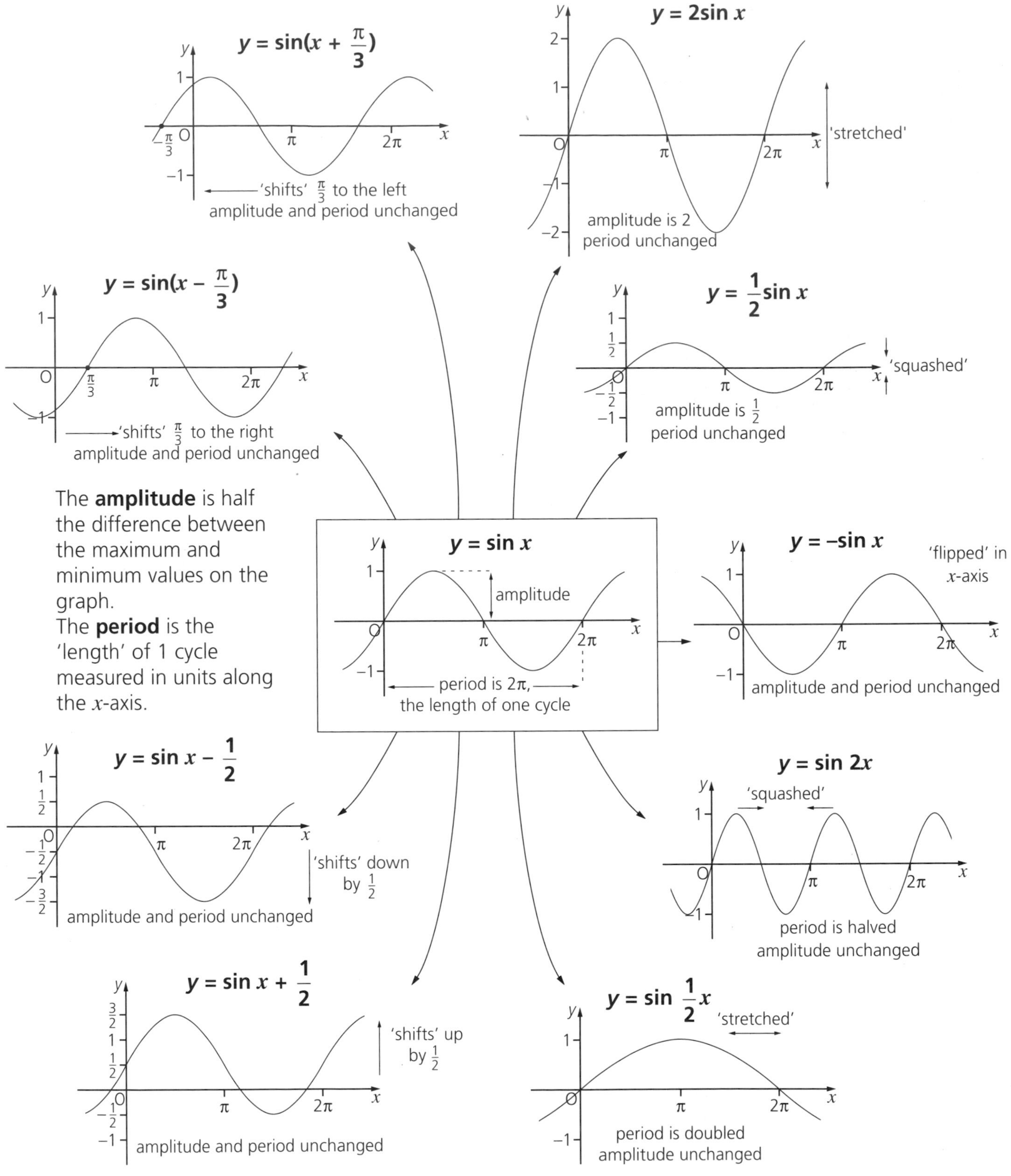

In Summary

Here is a description of the effect to the graphs $y = \cos x$ or $y = \sin x$

$$y = a \cos (bx \pm c) \pm d$$
$$y = a \sin (bx \pm c) \pm d$$

If $a > 0$ the amplitude is a. If $a < 0$ the graph 'flips' in the x-axis. The amplitude is the magnitude of a (ie ignore the negative sign).

Alters the period to $\frac{2\pi}{b}$ $(b > 0)$

'Shifts' the graph by c units left for $+ c$ or right for $- c$

'Shifts' the graph by d units up for $+ d$ or down for $- d$

example 10.1

Find the coordinates of the minimum turning point on the graph $y = 5\cos(x + \frac{\pi}{6})$ for $0 \le x \le \pi$

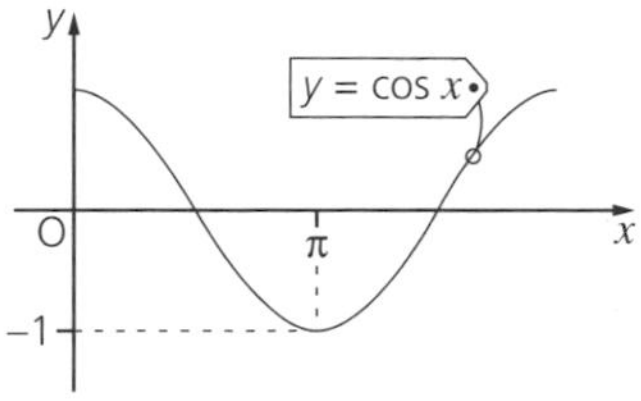

solution:

The minimum value is –5 when

$\cos(x + \frac{\pi}{6}) = -1$

ie when $x + \frac{\pi}{6} = \pi$

This gives $x = \pi - \frac{\pi}{6} = \frac{6\pi}{6} - \frac{\pi}{6} = \frac{5\pi}{6}$

Required minimum point is $\left(\mathbf{\frac{5\pi}{6}, -5}\right)$

example 10.2

The diagram shows part of the graph of $y = a\sin(x - b) + c$. Find the values of a, b and c.

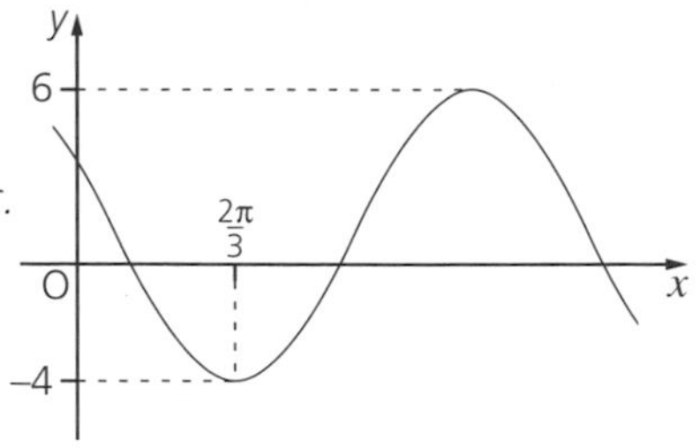

solution:

Compared with $y = \sin x$... The amplitude is 5 (half the difference between –4 and 6). However the graph is 'flipped' in the x-axis so $\mathbf{a = -5}$.
Also the graph has moved up 1 (max/min 6 and –4 instead of 5 and –5) so $\mathbf{c = 1}$.
It has also moved to the right: $\frac{2\pi}{3}$ instead of $\frac{\pi}{2}$

...now $\frac{2\pi}{3} - \frac{\pi}{2} = \frac{4\pi}{6} - \frac{3\pi}{6} = \frac{\pi}{6}$

so $\mathbf{b = \frac{\pi}{6}}$. The graph is $y = -5\sin(x - \frac{\pi}{6}) + 1$

The Addition Formulae

sin (A + B) = sin A cos B + cos A sin B
sin (A – B) = sin A cos B – cos A sin B
cos (A + B) = cos A cos B – sin A sin B
cos (A – B) = cos A cos B + sin A sin B

example 10.3

Show that $\cos(90 + x)° = -\sin x°$

solution:

$\cos(90 + x)° = \cos 90° \cos x° - \sin 90° \sin x°$
$= 0 \times \cos x° - 1 \times \sin x° = \mathbf{-\sin x°}$

example 10.4

If A and B are acute angles with $\sin A = \frac{3}{5}$ and $\cos B = \frac{12}{13}$ find the **exact** value of cos(A + B).

solution:

Draw right-angled triangles showing ∠A and ∠B (use Pythagoras' Theorem to find third side).

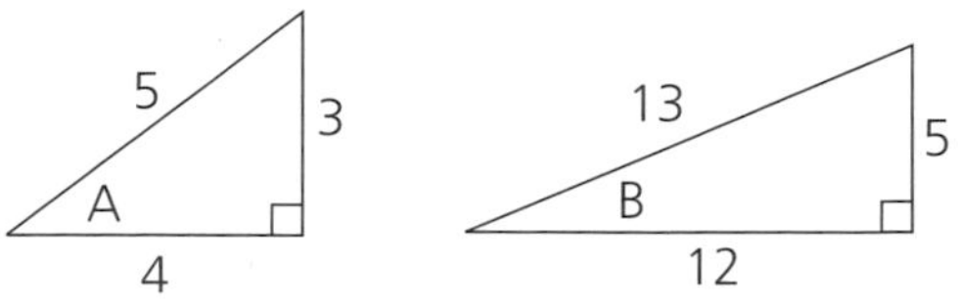

Then $\cos(A + B) = \cos A \cos B - \sin A \sin B$

$= \frac{4}{5} \times \frac{12}{13} - \frac{3}{5} \times \frac{5}{13}$

$= \frac{48}{65} - \frac{15}{65} = \mathbf{\frac{33}{65}}$

The Double Angle Formulae

sin 2A = 2sin A cos A

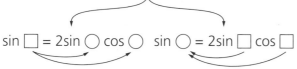

sin □ = 2sin ○ cos ○ — The ○ angles are half the size of the □ angle.

sin ○ = 2sin □ cos □ — The ○ angle is twice the size of the □ angles.

examples: $\sin 4\theta = 2\sin 2\theta \cos 2\theta$

$\sin P = 2\sin \frac{P}{2} \cos \frac{P}{2}$

cos 2A = 2cos² A – 1
or **cos² A – sin² A**
or **1 – 2sin² A**

Rearrangement gives:

$\cos^2 A = \frac{1}{2}(1 + \cos 2A)$ or $\sin^2 A = \frac{1}{2}(1 - \cos 2A)$

Formulae Reminders

$\mathbf{\sin^2 A + \cos^2 A = 1}$ → $\sin^2 A = 1 - \cos^2 A$ and $\cos^2 A = 1 - \sin^2 A$

$$\frac{\sin A}{\cos A} = \tan A$$

Some Related Angles

$\sin(-A)^\circ = -\sin A^\circ$ $\quad$ $\sin(180 - A)^\circ = \sin A^\circ$

$\cos(-A)^\circ = \cos A^\circ$ $\quad$ $\cos(180 - A)^\circ = -\cos A^\circ$

These and other similar results can be deduced from the quadrant diagram or by using the addition formulae.

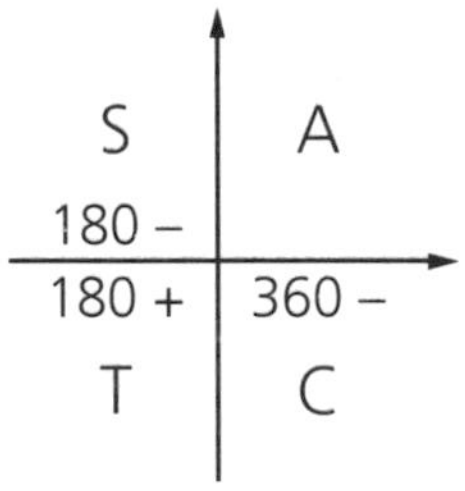

$\sin(90 - A)^\circ = \cos A^\circ$ $\quad$ $\cos(90 - A)^\circ = \sin A^\circ$

Triangle Problems

Useful results are:

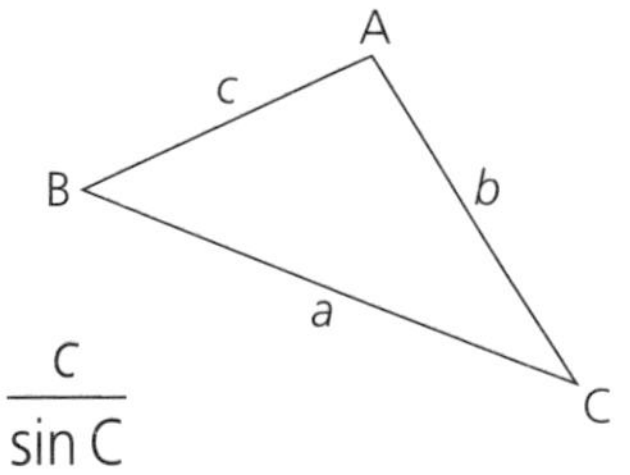

Sine Rule:

$$\frac{a}{\sin A} = \frac{b}{\sin B} = \frac{c}{\sin C}$$

Cosine Rule:

$a^2 = b^2 + c^2 - 2bc \cos A$

or $\quad b^2 = a^2 + c^2 - 2ac \cos B$

or $\quad c^2 = a^2 + b^2 - 2ab \cos C$

Area of triangle $= \frac{1}{2}ab \sin C$

or $\quad \frac{1}{2}bc \sin A$

or $\quad \frac{1}{2}ac \sin B$

Note that $\angle A = 180^\circ - (\angle B + \angle C)$...

example 10.5

If $\tan\alpha = \frac{\sqrt{7}}{2}$ find the **exact** value of $\sin 2\alpha$.

solution:

Here is a right-angled triangle:

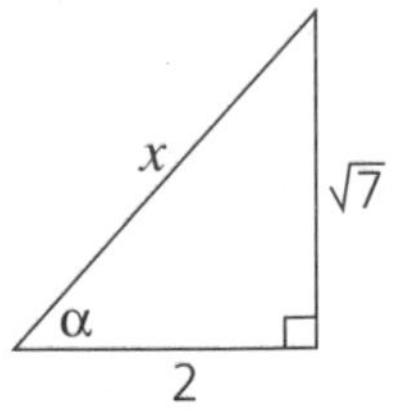

$x^2 = 2^2 + (\sqrt{7})^2$

$= 4 + 7 = 11$

So $\quad x = \sqrt{11}$

Thus $\sin 2\alpha = 2\sin\alpha\cos\alpha = 2 \times \frac{\sqrt{7}}{\sqrt{11}} \times \frac{2}{\sqrt{11}} = \mathbf{\frac{4\sqrt{7}}{11}}$

example 10.6

Show that $(\cos x + \sin x)^2 = 1 + \sin 2x$.

solution:

$(\cos x + \sin x)^2 = (\cos x + \sin x)(\cos x + \sin x)$

$= \cos^2 x + \cos x \sin x + \sin x \cos x + \sin^2 x$

$= \cos^2 x + \sin^2 x + 2\sin x \cos x$

$= \quad 1 \quad + \quad \sin 2x$

example 10.7

In triangle ABC prove that

$$\frac{a}{\sin 2x^\circ} = \frac{b}{\sin x^\circ}$$

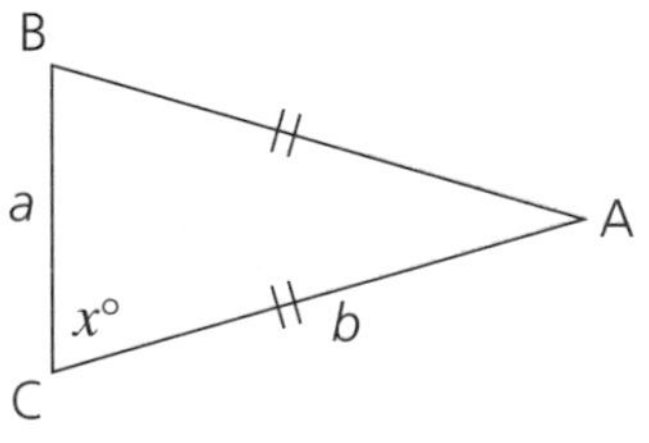

solution:

$\angle B = x^\circ$ (triangle ABC is isosceles)

so $\quad \angle A = 180^\circ - (x^\circ + x^\circ) = 180^\circ - 2x^\circ$

The Sine Rule gives $\quad \frac{a}{\sin A} = \frac{b}{\sin B}$

so $\quad \frac{a}{\sin(180 - 2x)^\circ} = \frac{b}{\sin x^\circ}$

But $\sin(180 - 2x)^\circ = \sin 2x^\circ$ hence $\mathbf{\frac{a}{\sin 2x^\circ} = \frac{b}{\sin x^\circ}}$

Solving Trig Equations

The **General Method** is...

Complicated = Complicated

↓ rearrange

Complicated = 0

↓ rearrange

Complicated = 0
(but can now be factorised!)

↓ factorise

(simpler)(simpler) = 0

simpler = 0 or simpler = 0

↓ solve ↓ solve

The Double Angle formulae may be useful in rearranging to produce an expression that can be factorised.

A **particular example** is...

Solve $\cos 2x° + 3 = 5(1 + \cos x°)$ for $0 \le x \le 360$

$$\cos 2x° + 3 = 5 + 5\cos x°$$

$$\cos 2x° - 5\cos x° - 2 = 0$$

$$2\cos^2 x° - 1 - 5\cos x° - 2 = 0$$

$$2\cos^2 x° - 5\cos x° - 3 = 0$$

(a quadratic in $\cos x°$)

$$(2\cos x° + 1)(\cos x° - 3) = 0$$

$2\cos x° + 1 = 0$ or $\cos x° - 3 = 0$

$2\cos x° = -1$ $\quad$ $\cos x° = 3$

$\cos x° = -\frac{1}{2}$ $\quad$ no solutions

($x°$ is in 2nd or 3rd quads) (since $-1 \le \cos x° \le 1$)

(1st quad angle is 60°)

so $x° = 180° - 60°$ or $180° + 60°$

$\mathbf{x° = 120°}$ **or** $\mathbf{240°}$

example 10.8

Find the coordinates of point P, the point of intersection of the two graphs in the diagram.

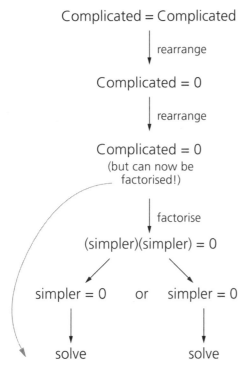

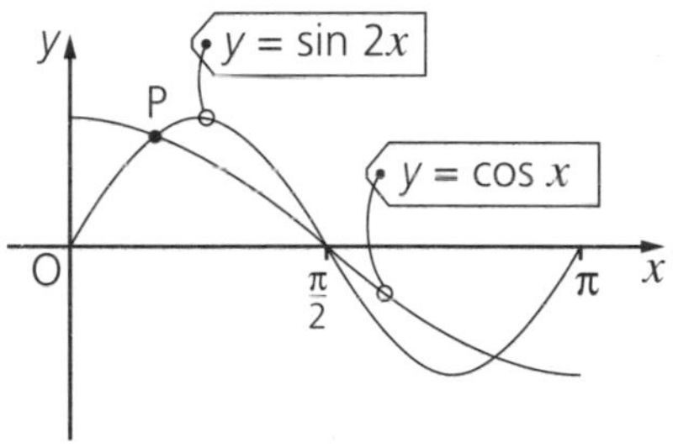

solution:

For points of intersection solve:

$$\sin 2x = \cos x$$

$$\sin 2x - \cos x = 0$$

$$2\sin x \cos x - \cos x = 0$$

$$\cos x\,(2\sin x - 1) = 0$$

$\cos x = 0$ $\quad$ $2\sin x - 1 = 0$

$x = \frac{\pi}{2}, \frac{3\pi}{2}, \ldots$ $\quad$ $\sin x = \frac{1}{2}$

$$x = \frac{\pi}{6}, \pi - \frac{\pi}{6}, \ldots$$

$$= \frac{\pi}{6}, \frac{5\pi}{6}, \ldots$$

when $x = \frac{\pi}{6}$, $y = \cos\frac{\pi}{6} = \frac{\sqrt{3}}{2}$ (exact value)

Required point is $\mathbf{P\left(\frac{\pi}{6}, \frac{\sqrt{3}}{2}\right)}$

The Angle Between a Line and Plane

If QR is the **projection** or 'vertical shadow' of line PQ on the plane then

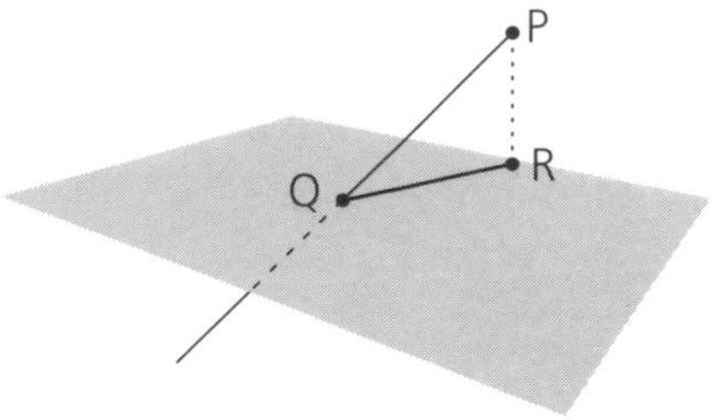

∠PQR is the angle between the line and plane.

The Angle Between Two Planes

Choose a point B on the line l where the two planes meet. Draw AB on one plane and BC on the other, both perpendicular to line l.

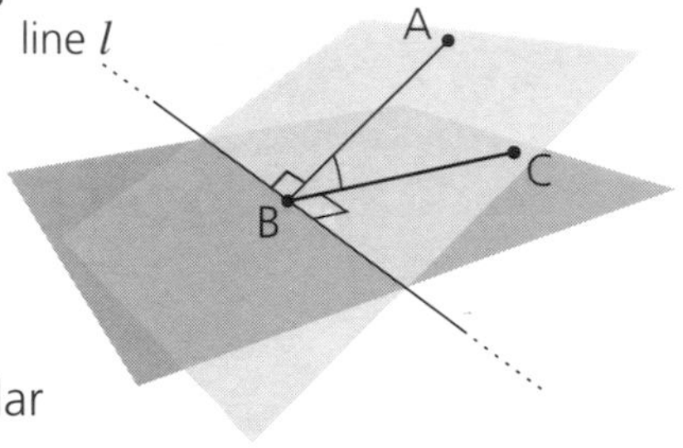

∠ABC is the angle between the two planes.

example 10.9

A square-based pyramid has vertex P, 3 metres above Q, the centre of the base. The square base has side length 6 metres.

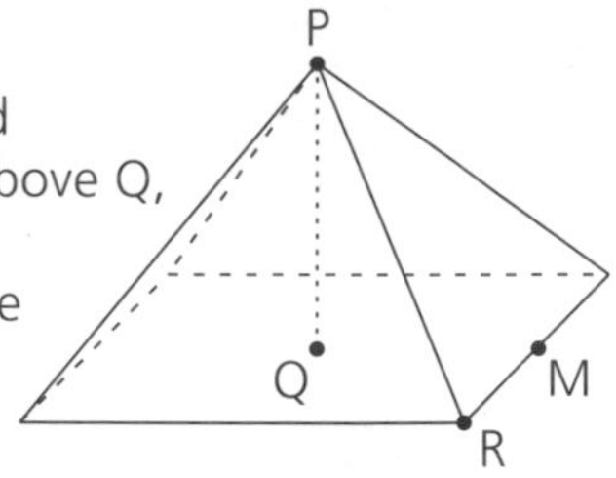

a) Find the angle between the base and a sloping face in radians.

solution:
Choose M, the midpoint of one of the sides of the square base.

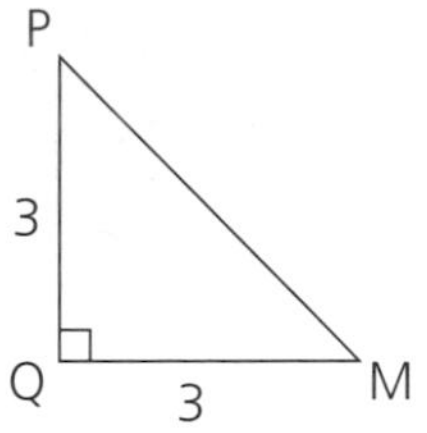

Required angle is $\angle QMP = \frac{\pi}{4}$
(isosceles right-angled triangle).

b) Find the angle between one of the sloping edges and the base in radians.

solution:
Choose R, one of the vertices of the square base. QR is half of the diagonal of the base, so QR = $3\sqrt{2}$

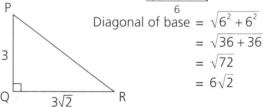

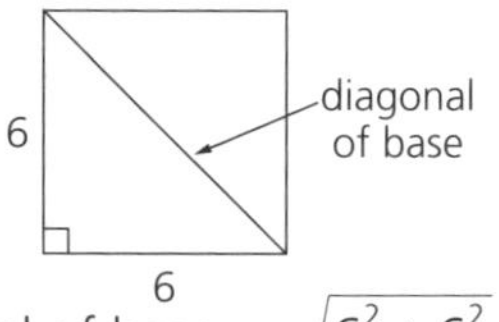

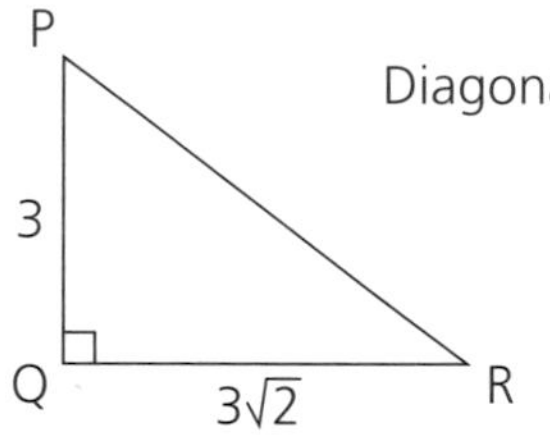

$$\text{Diagonal of base} = \sqrt{6^2+6^2} = \sqrt{36+36} = \sqrt{72} = 6\sqrt{2}$$

Required angle is

$\angle PRQ$ and $\tan \angle PRQ = \frac{3}{3\sqrt{2}} = \frac{1}{\sqrt{2}}$

(Put calculator in Radian Mode) giving
$\angle PRQ =$ **0·615** radians (to 3 sig. figs.).

A Circle Centre the Origin

The equation of a circle centre the origin with radius r is

$$x^2 + y^2 = r^2$$

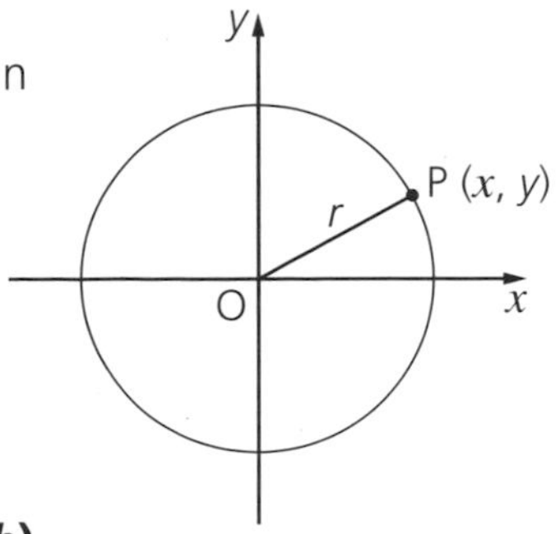

A Circle Centre (a, b)

The equation of a circle centre (a, b) with radius r is

$$(x - a)^2 + (y - b)^2 = r^2$$

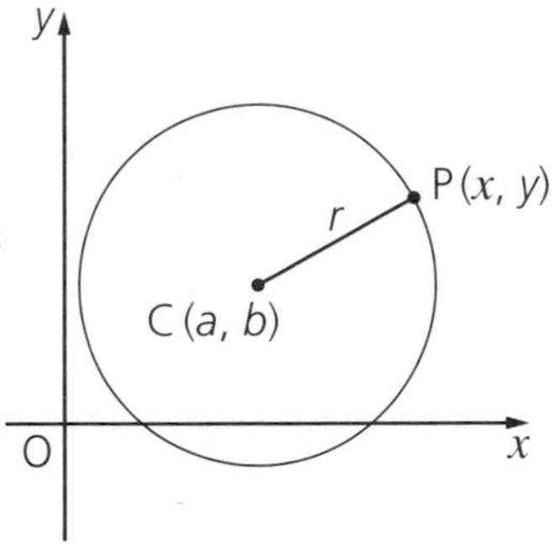

The General Equation of the Circle

In general any equation of a circle can be rearranged to look like:

$$x^2 + y^2 + ax + by + c = 0$$

halve and change sign (a, b)

Centre is $\left(-\frac{a}{2}, -\frac{b}{2}\right)$

square and add; subtract (c)

Radius is $\sqrt{\left(-\frac{a}{2}\right)^2 + \left(-\frac{b}{2}\right)^2 - c}$

or

$$x^2 + y^2 + 2gx + 2fy + c = 0$$

halve and change sign

Centre is $(-g, -f)$

square and add; subtract

Radius is $\sqrt{g^2 + f^2 - c}$

note:
There must be a **positive** number under the square root sign.

example 11.1

The circle centre $(1, -4)$ with radius 5 units, cuts the x-axis at points A and B. Find the length of AB.

solution:

Centre is $(1, -4)$ Radius = 5

The equation is $(x - 1)^2 + (y + 4)^2 = 5^2$

ie $(x - 1)^2 + (y + 4)^2 = 25$

For x-axis intercepts set $y = 0$

so $(x - 1)^2 + 4^2 = 25 \Rightarrow (x - 1)^2 = 9 \Rightarrow x - 1 = \pm 3$

giving $x = \pm 3 + 1$ so $x = 4$ or -2.

Thus **AB = 6 units**.

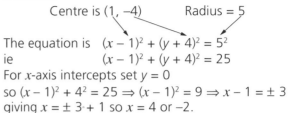

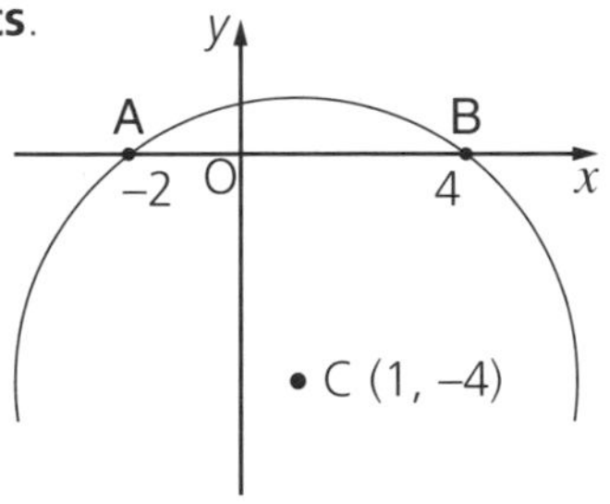

example 11.2

Find the centre and radius of the circle
$x^2 + y^2 - 2x + 3y - 3 = 0$

solution:

$$x^2 + y^2 - 2x + 3y - 3 = 0$$

Centre is $\left(1, -\frac{3}{2}\right)$

Radius $= \sqrt{1^2 + \left(-\frac{3}{2}\right)^2 - (-3)}$

$= \sqrt{1 + \frac{9}{4} + 3} = \sqrt{\frac{25}{4}} = \mathbf{\frac{5}{2}}$

example 11.3

For what range of values of k does
$x^2 + y^2 - 2x + 6y + k = 0$ represent a circle?

solution:

Centre is $(1, -3)$

Radius $= \sqrt{1^2 + (-3)^2 - k} = \sqrt{10 - k}$

So $10 - k > 0$ ie $10 > k$ or $\boldsymbol{k < 10}$
(or there's no circle!)

11. Circles

A Line and a Circle

To find points of intersection of a line and a circle you solve their equations simultaneously. This will result in a quadratic equation. Three distinct situations can arise…

2 points of intersection

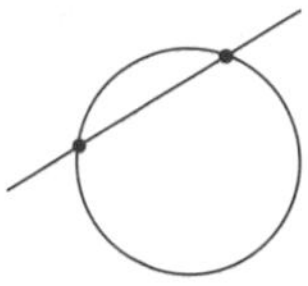

solve:
equation of line
equation of circle }

⇓

quadratic equation
with 2 roots

Discriminant > 0

1 point of intersection

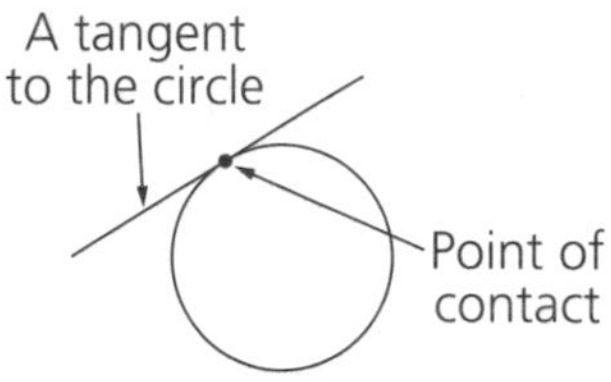

solve:
equation of line
equation of circle }

⇓

quadratic equation
with 1 root
(equal roots)
Discriminant = 0

No points of intersection

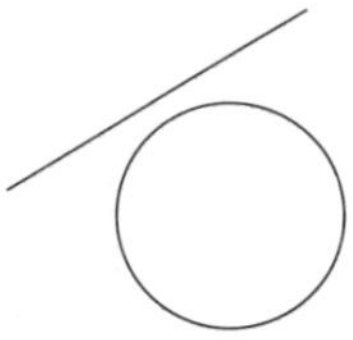

solve:
equation of line
equation of circle }

⇓

quadratic equation
with no Real roots

Discriminant < 0

example 11.4

Show that $y = 2x - 10$ is a tangent to the circle $x^2 + y^2 - 4x + 2y = 0$ and find the point of contact.

solution:

For the points of intersection solve:

$$\left.\begin{array}{l} y = 2x - 10 \\ x^2 + y^2 - 4x + 2y = 0 \end{array}\right\} \Rightarrow$$ Substitute $y = 2x - 10$ in the circle equation.

This gives… $x^2 + (2x - 10)^2 - 4x + 2(2x - 10) = 0$

$$x^2 + 4x^2 - 40x + 100 - 4x + 4x - 20 = 0$$
$$5x^2 - 40x + 80 = 0$$
$$5(x^2 - 8x + 16) = 0$$
$$5(x - 4)(x - 4) = 0$$

giving **only one solution**, $x = 4$, so **the line is a tangent**.

when $x = 4$, $y = 2 \times 4 - 10 = 8 - 10 = -2$
so the **Point of Contact is (4, –2)**.

Where is the Centre?

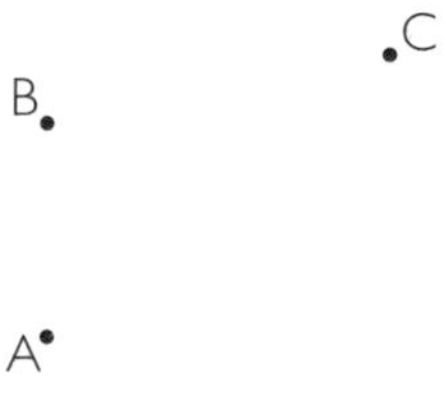

Given three points A, B and C where is the centre of the circle that passes through them?

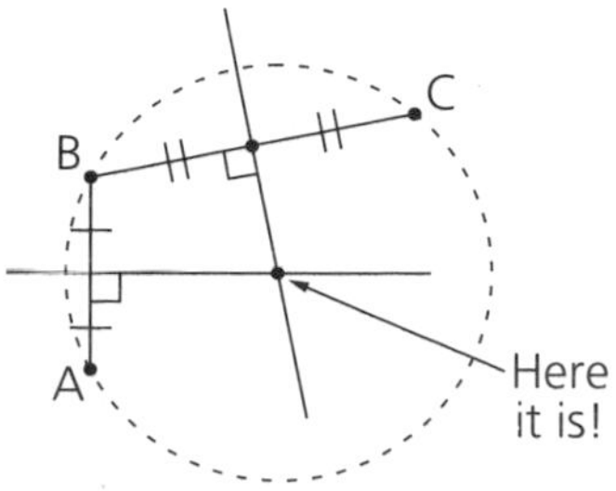

It is at the point of intersection of the perpendicular bisectors of AB and BC. These lines are **chords** of the required circle.

example 11.5

$y = mx$ is a tangent to the circle $(x + 2)^2 + y^2 = 3$
Find the possible values of m

solution:
The points of intersection can be found by solving:

$$\left.\begin{array}{l} y = mx \\ (x+2)^2 + y^2 = 3 \end{array}\right\} \Rightarrow \begin{array}{r} (x+2)^2 + (mx)^2 = 3 \\ x^2 + 4x + 4 + m^2x^2 = 3 \\ (1+m^2)x^2 + 4x + 1 = 0 \end{array}$$

This is a quadratic equation in x...

$$\begin{aligned} \text{Discriminant} &= 4^2 - 4(1+m^2) \times 1 \\ \text{('}b^2-4ac\text{')} \quad &= 16 - 4 - 4m^2 \\ &= 12 - 4m^2 \end{aligned}$$

For the line to be a tangent the quadratic equation must have 1 root (or equal roots) so...

Discriminant = 0 giving $12 - 4m^2 = 0$

$\Rightarrow m^2 = 3 \Rightarrow m = \sqrt{3}$ or $-\sqrt{3}$

[Check with a diagram. The circle has centre (–2, 0) and radius = $\sqrt{3}$ ...

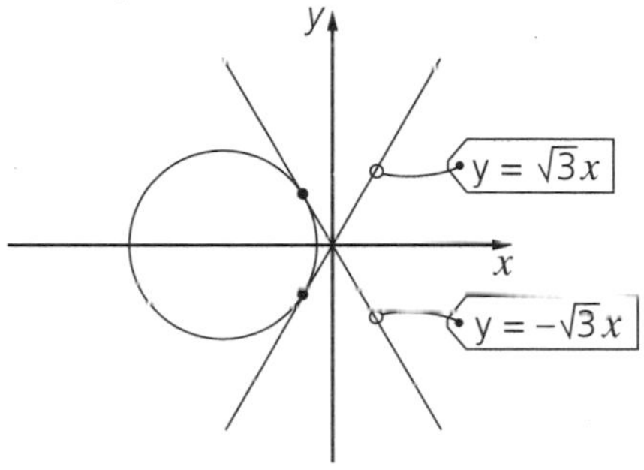

The two possible tangents are shown.]

Touching Circles

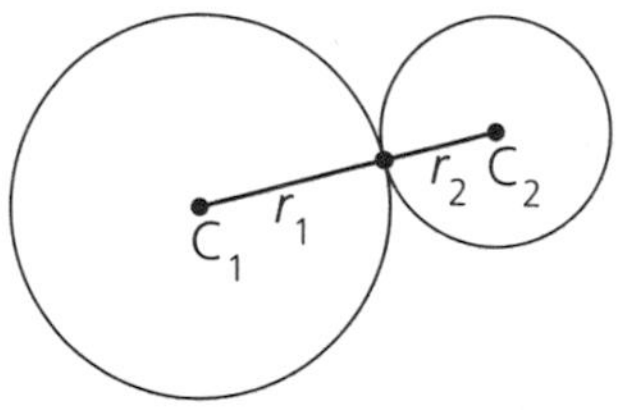

To determine whether two circles 'touch' externally as shown in the diagram:

step 1 Calculate C_1C_2, the distance between the centres.

step 2 Calculate $r_1 + r_2$, the sum of the radii.

step 3 Compare values. If $C_1C_2 = r_1 + r_2$ then the circles touch.

example 11.6

Determine whether or not the circles with equations $(x + 1)^2 + (y - 2)^2 = 8$ and $(x - 6)^2 + (y - 1)^2 = 18$ touch.

solution:

For $(x + 1)^2 + (y - 2)^2 = 8$: C_1 (–1, 2) and $r_1 = \sqrt{8} = 2\sqrt{2}$

For $(x - 6)^2 + (y - 1)^2 = 18$: C_2 (6, 1) and $r_2 = \sqrt{18} = 3\sqrt{2}$

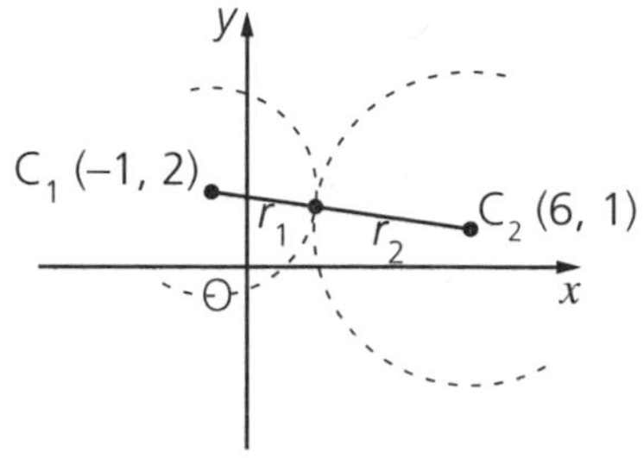

$$\begin{aligned} \text{Now } C_1C_2 &= \sqrt{(-1-6)^2 + (2-1)^2} \\ &= \sqrt{49+1} = \sqrt{50} = 5\sqrt{2} \\ \text{also } r_1 + r_2 &= 2\sqrt{2} + 3\sqrt{2} = 5\sqrt{2} \end{aligned}$$

Thus $C_1C_2 = r_1 + r_2$ and so **the circles touch**.

3-Dimensional Coordinates

To locate a point P in space requires three coordinates. For example...

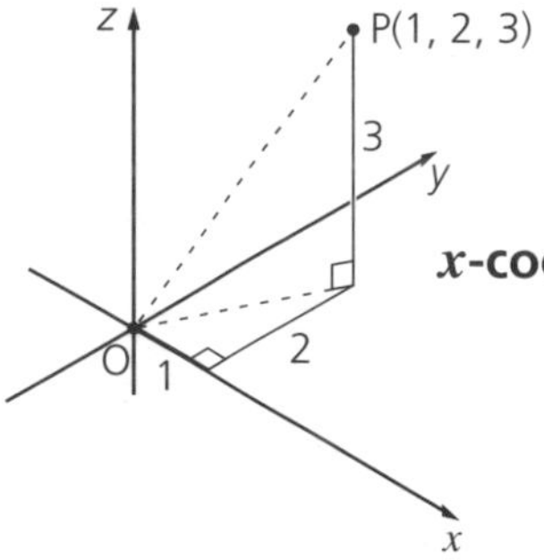

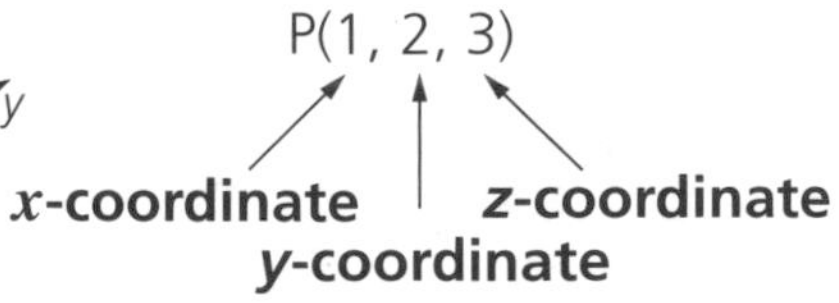

Think of (1, 2, 3) as the 'address' of point P.

What is a Vector?

A vector is a quantity with both **magnitude** and **direction**. It can be represented by a **directed line segment**.

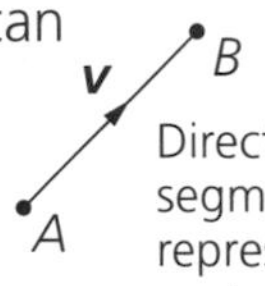

Directed line segment AB represents the vector ***v***.

Examples of vector quantities are:
velocity, magnetic field strength, push/pull forces etc.

Components

Vectors are described using components parallel to the x-, y- and z-axes. In the diagram, vector ***v***, represented by $\overrightarrow{AB}$, has components $\begin{pmatrix}1\\2\\3\end{pmatrix}$.

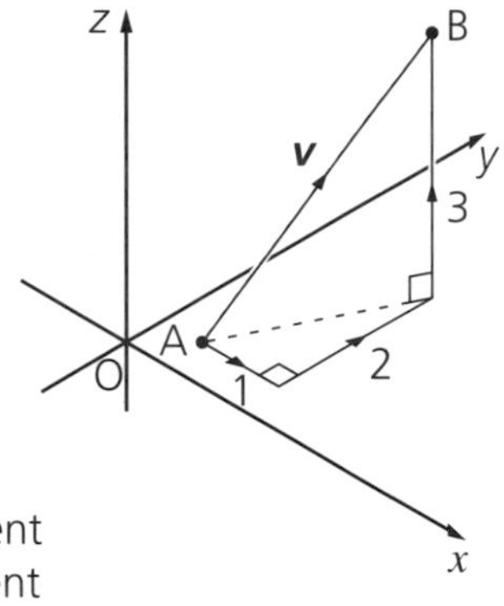

$\boldsymbol{v} = \begin{pmatrix}1\\2\\3\end{pmatrix}$ ← x-component, ← y-component, ← z-component

Think of $\begin{pmatrix}1\\2\\3\end{pmatrix}$ as the 'instructions for a journey'.

It describes any journey that goes the same distance and direction as the journey from A to B.

Magnitude

The **magnitude** (length) of a vector $\boldsymbol{v} = \begin{pmatrix}a\\b\\c\end{pmatrix}$ is given by

$|\boldsymbol{v}| = \sqrt{a^2 + b^2 + c^2}$

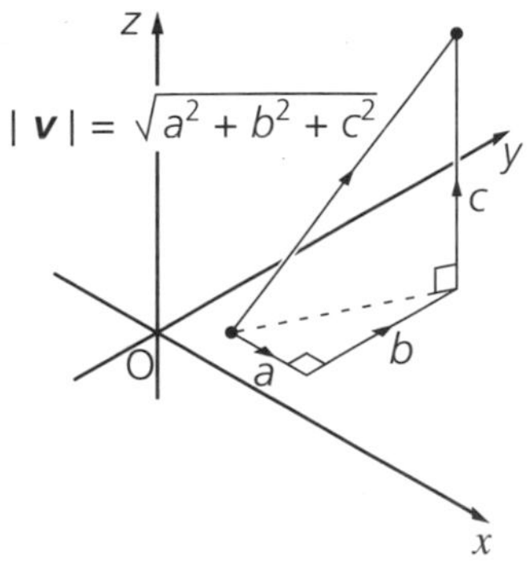

example 12.1

a) Write down the coordinates of B, C and D.

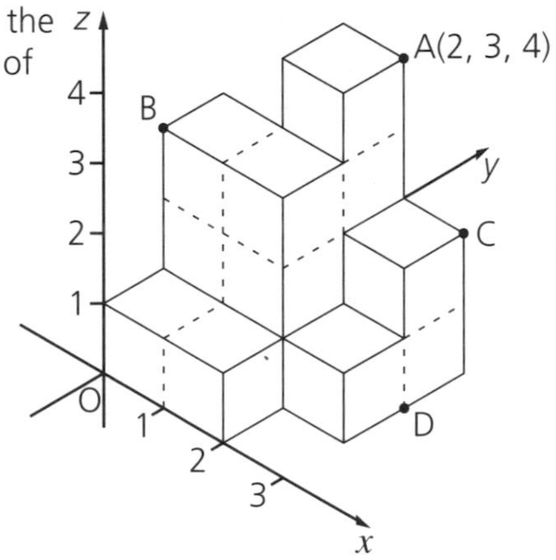

solution:
B (0, 1, 3)
C (3, 3, 2),
D (3, 2, 0)

b) Write down the components of $\overrightarrow{OA}$, $\overrightarrow{DC}$ and $\overrightarrow{DB}$.

solution:

$\overrightarrow{OA} = \begin{pmatrix}2\\3\\4\end{pmatrix}$ (components are same as coordinates)

$\overrightarrow{DC} = \begin{pmatrix}0\\1\\2\end{pmatrix}$ (1 along parallel to y-axis and 2 up parallel to z-axis)

$\overrightarrow{DB} = \begin{pmatrix}-3\\-1\\3\end{pmatrix}$ (3 in the **negative** direction of the x-axis, 1 in the **negative** direction of the y-axis, 3 up the z-axis)

example 12.2

Find the magnitude of $\boldsymbol{a} = \begin{pmatrix}-2\\3\\6\end{pmatrix}$

solution:

$|\boldsymbol{a}| = \sqrt{(-2)^2 + 3^2 + 6^2} = \sqrt{4 + 9 + 36}$
$= \sqrt{49}$
$= \mathbf{7}$

Equal Vectors

Each of these 'journeys' has the same distance and same direction and so represents the same vector ***a***.

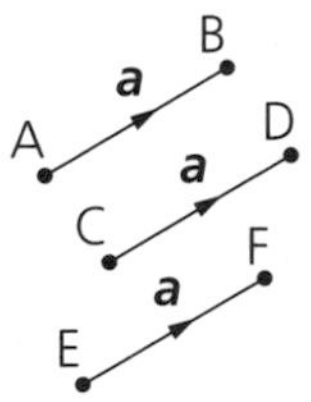

If $\overrightarrow{AB} = \overrightarrow{CD}$ then AB = CD and AB II CD
(equal directed line segments) (lengths equal) (parallel)

If $\begin{pmatrix} x_1 \\ y_1 \\ z_1 \end{pmatrix} = \begin{pmatrix} x_2 \\ y_2 \\ z_2 \end{pmatrix}$ then $x_1 = x_2, y_1 = y_2, z_1 = z_2$
(equal vectors) (equal components)

Vector Addition

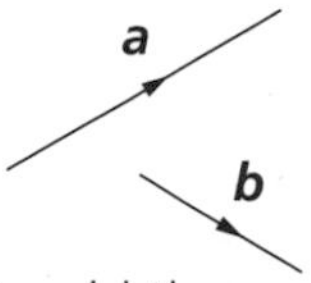

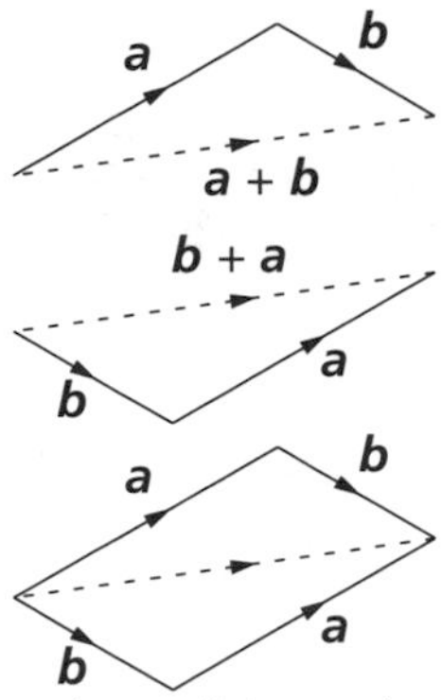

(a parallelogram)

To add these vectors place them 'nose-to-tail'.
Notice that ***a*** + ***b*** = ***b*** + ***a***
Using components...

if ***a*** = $\begin{pmatrix} x_1 \\ y_1 \\ z_1 \end{pmatrix}$ and ***b*** = $\begin{pmatrix} x_2 \\ y_2 \\ z_2 \end{pmatrix}$

then ***a*** + ***b*** = $\begin{pmatrix} x_1 \\ y_1 \\ z_1 \end{pmatrix} + \begin{pmatrix} x_2 \\ y_2 \\ z_2 \end{pmatrix} = \begin{pmatrix} x_1+x_2 \\ y_1+y_2 \\ z_1+z_2 \end{pmatrix}$

(Add the corresponding components.)

The Zero Vector

$\mathbf{0} = \begin{pmatrix} 0 \\ 0 \\ 0 \end{pmatrix}$ The zero vector has magnitude | **0** | = 0 but has **no** direction defined.

The Negative of a Vector

–***a*** has the same magnitude as ***a*** but the opposite direction

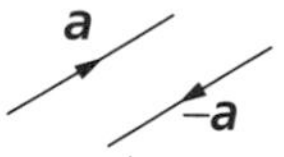

(reverse the arrow)

and using components...

if ***a*** = $\begin{pmatrix} x_1 \\ y_1 \\ z_1 \end{pmatrix}$ then –***a*** = $\begin{pmatrix} -x_1 \\ -y_1 \\ -z_1 \end{pmatrix}$

Notice that ***a*** + (–***a***) = **0** the zero vector.

Vector Subtraction

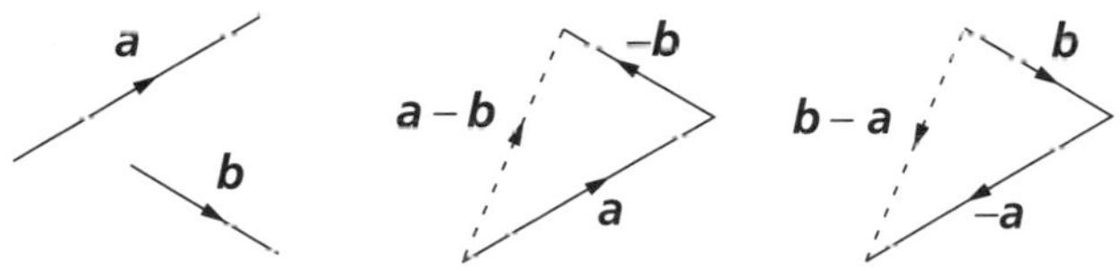

a – ***b*** is the vector ***a*** +(–***b***)
b – ***a*** is the vector ***b*** +(–***a***)
Notice that ***b*** – ***a*** = –(***a*** – ***b***)
Using components...

if ***a*** = $\begin{pmatrix} x_1 \\ y_1 \\ z_1 \end{pmatrix}$ and ***b*** = $\begin{pmatrix} x_2 \\ y_2 \\ z_2 \end{pmatrix}$

Then ***a*** – ***b*** = $\begin{pmatrix} x_1 \\ y_1 \\ z_1 \end{pmatrix} - \begin{pmatrix} x_2 \\ y_2 \\ z_2 \end{pmatrix} = \begin{pmatrix} x_1-x_2 \\ y_1-y_2 \\ z_1-z_2 \end{pmatrix}$

(Subtract the corresponding components.)

example 12.3

Calculate the magnitudes of ***a*** + ***b*** and ***a*** – ***b*** where
a = $\begin{pmatrix} -1 \\ 2 \\ 5 \end{pmatrix}$ and ***b*** = $\begin{pmatrix} 4 \\ -2 \\ -1 \end{pmatrix}$

solution:

$\mathbf{a} + \mathbf{b} = \begin{pmatrix} -1 \\ 2 \\ 5 \end{pmatrix} + \begin{pmatrix} 4 \\ -2 \\ -1 \end{pmatrix} = \begin{pmatrix} 3 \\ 0 \\ 4 \end{pmatrix}$

so $|\mathbf{a} + \mathbf{b}| = \sqrt{3^2 + 0^2 + 4^2} = \sqrt{25} = \mathbf{5}$

$\mathbf{a} - \mathbf{b} = \begin{pmatrix} -1 \\ 2 \\ 5 \end{pmatrix} - \begin{pmatrix} 4 \\ -2 \\ -1 \end{pmatrix} = \begin{pmatrix} -5 \\ 4 \\ 6 \end{pmatrix}$

so $|\mathbf{a} - \mathbf{b}| = \sqrt{(-5)^2 + 4^2 + 6^2}$
$= \sqrt{25 + 16 + 36} = \sqrt{\mathbf{77}}$

Scalar Multiplication

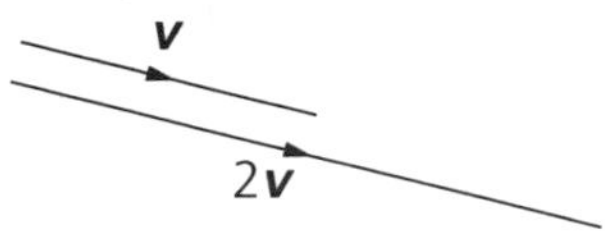

If ***v*** = $\begin{pmatrix} x_1 \\ y_1 \\ z_1 \end{pmatrix}$ then 2***v*** = ***v*** + ***v*** = $\begin{pmatrix} x_1 \\ y_1 \\ z_1 \end{pmatrix} + \begin{pmatrix} x_1 \\ y_1 \\ z_1 \end{pmatrix} = \begin{pmatrix} 2x_1 \\ 2y_1 \\ 2z_1 \end{pmatrix}$

In general $k\mathbf{v} = k\begin{pmatrix} x_1 \\ y_1 \\ z_1 \end{pmatrix} = \begin{pmatrix} kx_1 \\ ky_1 \\ kz_1 \end{pmatrix}$

The vector ***v*** has been multiplied by scalar *k* ('scalar' being number as opposed to vector).

Parallel Vectors

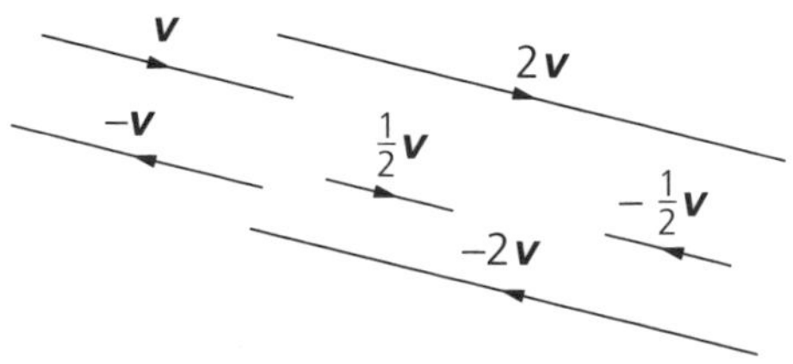

$\mathbf{a} = k\mathbf{b}$ $(k \neq 0)$ $\Longleftrightarrow$ ***a*** and ***b*** are parallel

If $k > 0$ they have the same direction.
If $k < 0$ they have opposite directions.

12. Vectors

Position Vectors

$\overrightarrow{OP}$, written $\boldsymbol{p}$, is the **position vector** of the point P.

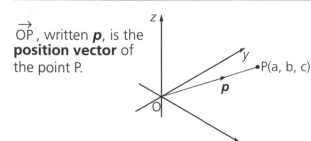

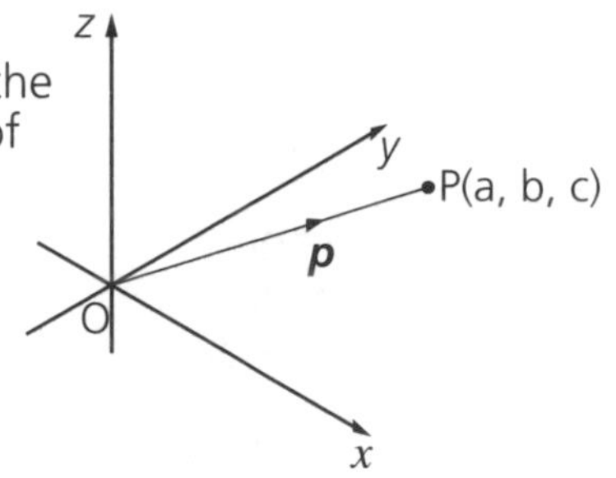

P(a, b, c) ⟷ $\boldsymbol{p} = \begin{pmatrix} a \\ b \\ c \end{pmatrix}$

(an 'address' using coordinates)

('instructions' for the journey from the origin to the point P).

$\overrightarrow{AB} = \boldsymbol{b} - \boldsymbol{a}$

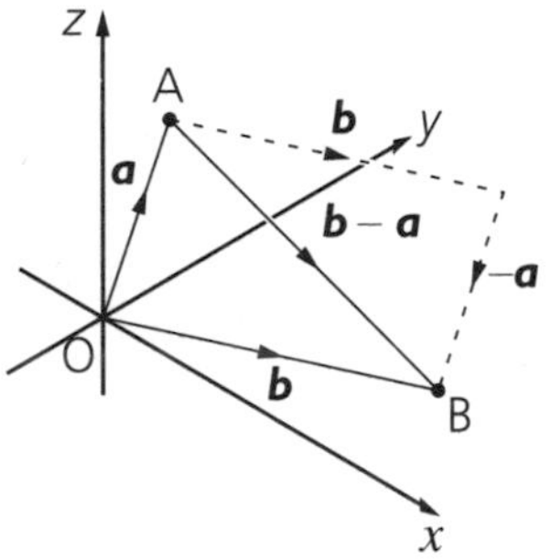

$\overrightarrow{AB} = \boldsymbol{b} - \boldsymbol{a}$

This is $\overrightarrow{AB}$ in terms of position vectors $\boldsymbol{a}$ and $\boldsymbol{b}$.

Similarly $\overrightarrow{PQ} = \boldsymbol{q} - \boldsymbol{p}$, $\overrightarrow{RS} = \boldsymbol{s} - \boldsymbol{r}$ etc

Collinear Points

To show three points A, B and C are **collinear** (share the same straight line) find the components of $\overrightarrow{AB}$ and of $\overrightarrow{BC}$ and compare them.

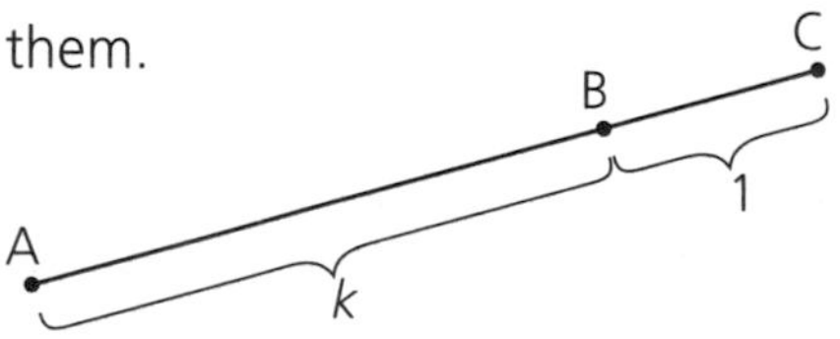

$\overrightarrow{AB} = k\overrightarrow{BC}$

or

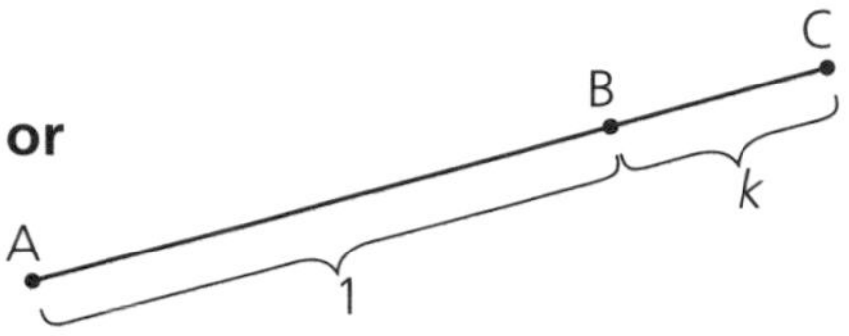

$\overrightarrow{BC} = k\overrightarrow{AB}$

If $\overrightarrow{AB} = k\overrightarrow{BC}$ (or $\overrightarrow{BC} = k\overrightarrow{AB}$)
(for a non-zero number k) then A, B and C are collinear.

example 12.4

P has coordinates (1, –1, 3) and Q has coordinates (–2, 5, 6). Find the components of $\overrightarrow{PQ}$.

solution:

In terms of position vectors

$$\overrightarrow{PQ} = \boldsymbol{q} - \boldsymbol{p}$$
$$= \begin{pmatrix} -2 \\ 5 \\ 6 \end{pmatrix} - \begin{pmatrix} 1 \\ -1 \\ 3 \end{pmatrix} = \begin{pmatrix} \mathbf{-3} \\ \mathbf{6} \\ \mathbf{3} \end{pmatrix}$$

example 12.5

Show that A(2, –1, –1), B(4, 3, –5) and C(5, 5, –7) are collinear and find the ratio in which B divides AC.

solution:

$$\overrightarrow{AB} = \boldsymbol{b} - \boldsymbol{a} = \begin{pmatrix} 4 \\ 3 \\ -5 \end{pmatrix} - \begin{pmatrix} 2 \\ -1 \\ -1 \end{pmatrix} = \begin{pmatrix} 2 \\ 4 \\ -4 \end{pmatrix}$$
$$\overrightarrow{BC} = \boldsymbol{c} - \boldsymbol{b} = \begin{pmatrix} 5 \\ 5 \\ -7 \end{pmatrix} - \begin{pmatrix} 4 \\ 3 \\ -5 \end{pmatrix} = \begin{pmatrix} 1 \\ 2 \\ -2 \end{pmatrix}$$
$$\overrightarrow{AB} = 2\overrightarrow{BC}$$

and, since B is a shared point, the points **A, B and C are collinear**.
Here is a diagram:

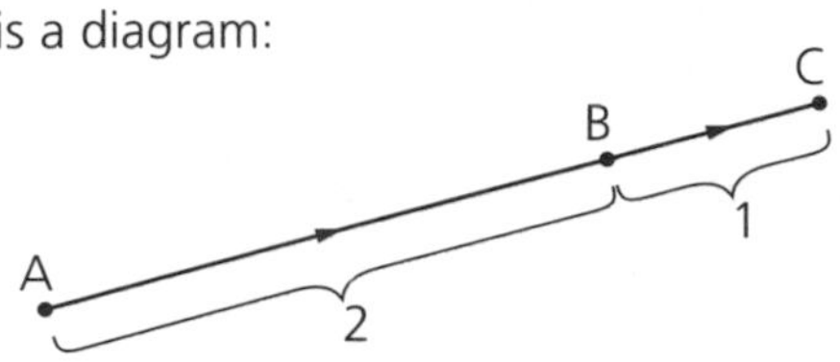

So B divides AC in the ratio **2:1**
Note that B divides CA in the ratio 1:2… the order is important.

The Midpoint

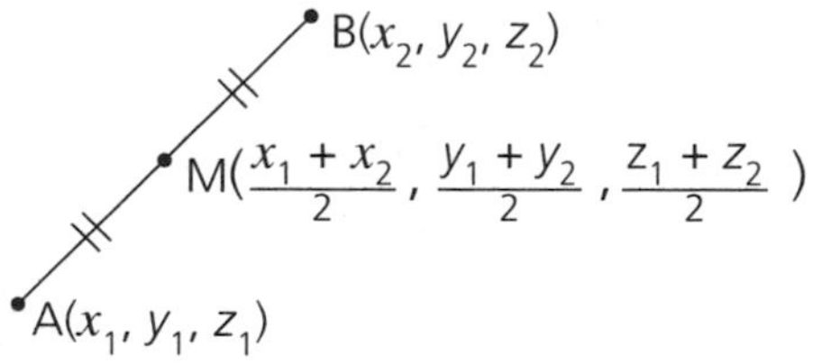

Take the 'average' of the corresponding coordinates and using position vectors...

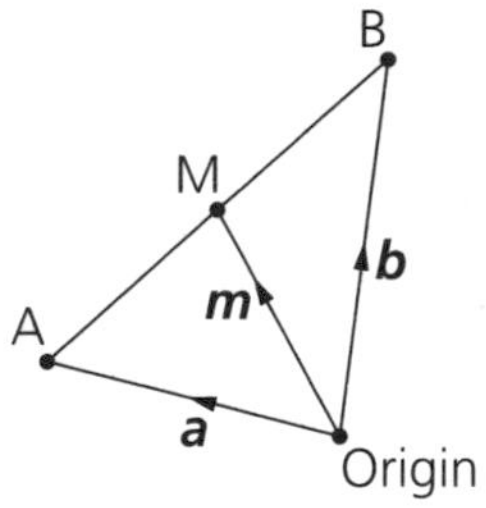

$$\boldsymbol{m} = \frac{1}{2}(\boldsymbol{a} + \boldsymbol{b})$$

example 12.6

Find the midpoint of AB where A is the point (1, –3, 2) and B is the point (2, 5, –1).

solution:

$$M\left(\frac{1+2}{2}, \frac{-3+5}{2}, \frac{2+(-1)}{2}\right) = \mathbf{M}\left(\frac{3}{2}, 1, \frac{1}{2}\right)$$

The Divided Line

If P divides AB in the ratio $m{:}n$

then $\overrightarrow{AP} = \frac{m}{m+n}\overrightarrow{AB}$

So $(m+n)\overrightarrow{AP} = m\overrightarrow{AB}$

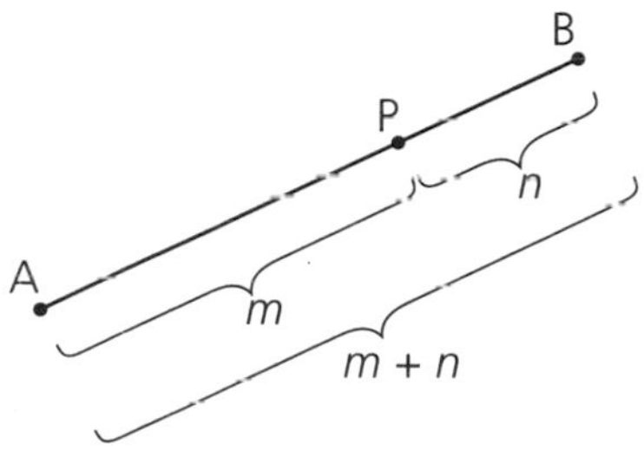

For example if Q divides PR in the ratio 3:2

then $\overrightarrow{PQ} = \frac{3}{5}\overrightarrow{PR}$

so $5\overrightarrow{PQ} = 3\overrightarrow{PR}$

or $\overrightarrow{RQ} = \frac{2}{5}\overrightarrow{RP}$

so $5\overrightarrow{RQ} = 2\overrightarrow{RP}$

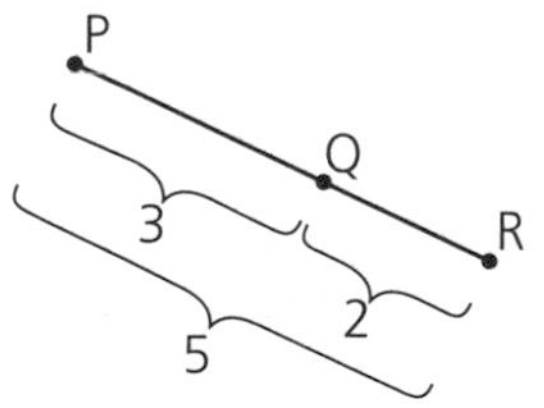

example 12.7

Find the coordinates of T the point which divides SU in the ratio 4:1, where S is the point (–1, 2, 6) and U is the point (4, –3, 1).

solution:

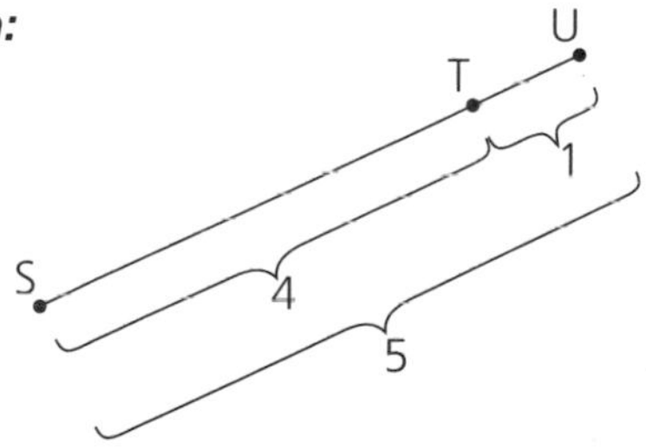

Think of 'journeys'.

The journey $\overrightarrow{ST}$ is $\frac{4}{5}$ of the whole journey $\overrightarrow{SU}$.

So $\overrightarrow{ST} = \frac{4}{5}\overrightarrow{SU}$ giving $5\overrightarrow{ST} = 4\overrightarrow{SU}$

Now use position vectors...

$5(\boldsymbol{t} - \boldsymbol{s}) = 4(\boldsymbol{u} - \boldsymbol{s})$

$5\boldsymbol{t} - 5\boldsymbol{s} = 4\boldsymbol{u} - 4\boldsymbol{s}$

$5\boldsymbol{t} = 4\boldsymbol{u} + \boldsymbol{s}$

The normal rules for algebra apply so solve to get ***t***.

So $5\boldsymbol{t} = 4\begin{pmatrix}4\\-3\\1\end{pmatrix} + \begin{pmatrix}-1\\2\\6\end{pmatrix} = \begin{pmatrix}15\\-10\\10\end{pmatrix}$ so $\boldsymbol{t} = \frac{1}{5}\begin{pmatrix}15\\-10\\10\end{pmatrix} = \begin{pmatrix}3\\-2\\2\end{pmatrix}$

Hence **T(3, –2, 2)** (coordinates asked for, not components).

12. Vectors

The Angle Between Vectors

Place the two vectors tail-to-tail:

θ is the angle between ***a*** and ***b***

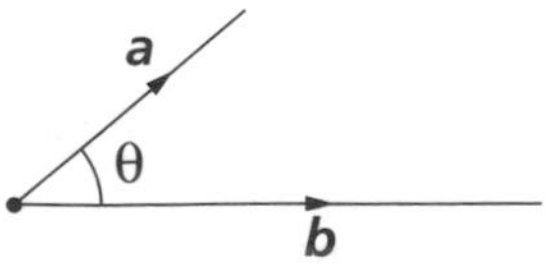

θ always lies in the range $0 \le \theta \le \pi$

Maximum angle is π

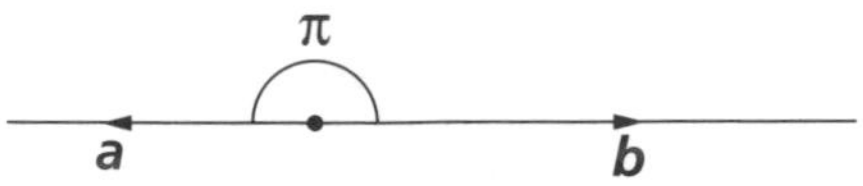

Minimum angle is 0

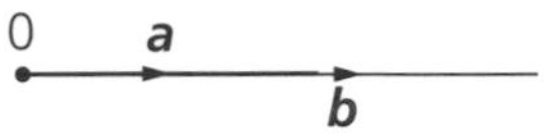

The Scalar or Dot Product

Using magnitudes and the angle…

$\mathbf{a.b} = |\,\mathbf{a}\,|\,|\,\mathbf{b}\,| \cos\theta$

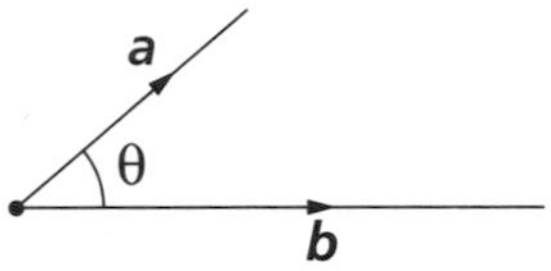

Using components…

$\mathbf{a.b} = x_1x_2 + y_1y_2 + z_1z_2$

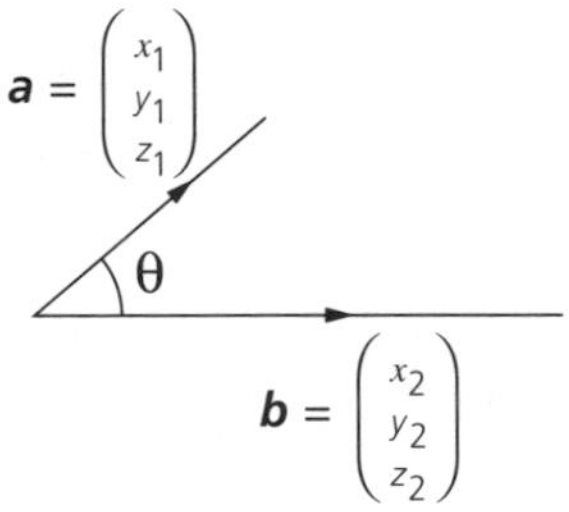

These two calculations yield the same **number** which is written ***a.b*** and is called either the **Scalar Product** or **Dot Product** of vectors ***a*** and ***b***.

Calculating the Angle

The angle θ between two non-zero vectors is found using…

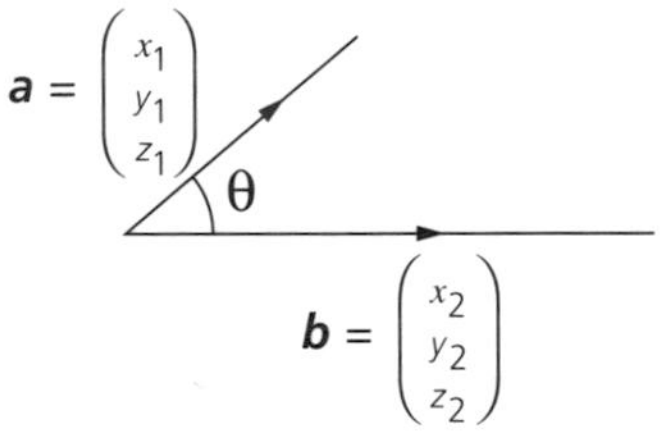

$$\cos\theta = \frac{x_1x_2 + y_1y_2 + z_1z_2}{\sqrt{x_1^2 + y_1^2 + z_1^2}\,\sqrt{x_2^2 + y_2^2 + z_2^2}} = \frac{\mathbf{a.b}}{|\,\mathbf{a}\,|\,|\,\mathbf{b}\,|}$$

(the Dot Product divided by the product of the magnitudes)

Perpendicular Vectors

If ***a.b*** = 0 and both ***a*** and ***b*** are non-zero then ***a*** is perpendicular to ***b***

Conversely:

If ***a*** and ***b*** are perpendicular then ***a.b*** = 0

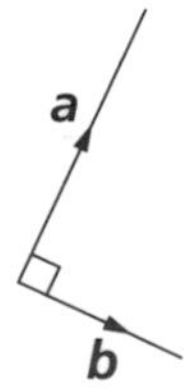

example 12.8

Calculate the angle θ between $\mathbf{a} = \begin{pmatrix} 2 \\ 3 \\ -1 \end{pmatrix}$ and $\mathbf{b} = \begin{pmatrix} 1 \\ -2 \\ 3 \end{pmatrix}$.

solution:

$|\,\mathbf{a}\,| = \sqrt{2^2 + 3^2 + (-1)^2} = \sqrt{14}$

$|\,\mathbf{b}\,| = \sqrt{1^2 + (-2)^2 + 3^2} = \sqrt{14}$

$\mathbf{a.b} = \begin{pmatrix} 2 \\ 3 \\ -1 \end{pmatrix}.\begin{pmatrix} 1 \\ -2 \\ 3 \end{pmatrix} = 2 \times 1 + 3 \times (-2) + (-1) \times 3 = -7$

so $\cos\theta = \dfrac{\mathbf{a.b}}{|\,\mathbf{a}\,|\,|\,\mathbf{b}\,|} = \dfrac{-7}{\sqrt{14}\sqrt{14}} = -\dfrac{7}{14} = -\dfrac{1}{2}$

so $\quad \theta = \pi - \dfrac{\pi}{3} = \mathbf{\dfrac{2\pi}{3}}$ (second quadrant only)

example 12.9

A triangle ABC has vertices A(–1, 3, 2), B(1, –3, 3) and C(0, 2, –6). Show that it is right-angled.

solution:

$\overrightarrow{AB} = \mathbf{b} - \mathbf{a} = \begin{pmatrix} 1 \\ -3 \\ 3 \end{pmatrix} - \begin{pmatrix} -1 \\ 3 \\ 2 \end{pmatrix} = \begin{pmatrix} 2 \\ -6 \\ 1 \end{pmatrix}$

$\overrightarrow{AC} = \mathbf{c} - \mathbf{a} = \begin{pmatrix} 0 \\ 2 \\ -6 \end{pmatrix} - \begin{pmatrix} -1 \\ 3 \\ 2 \end{pmatrix} = \begin{pmatrix} 1 \\ -1 \\ -8 \end{pmatrix}$

So

$\overrightarrow{AB}.\overrightarrow{AC} = \begin{pmatrix} 2 \\ -6 \\ 1 \end{pmatrix}.\begin{pmatrix} 1 \\ -1 \\ -8 \end{pmatrix} = 2 \times 1 + (-6) \times (-1) + 1 \times (-8) = 0$

hence $\overrightarrow{AB}$ is perpendicular to $\overrightarrow{AC}$

$\angle BAC = 90°$

So ΔABC is right-angled at A.

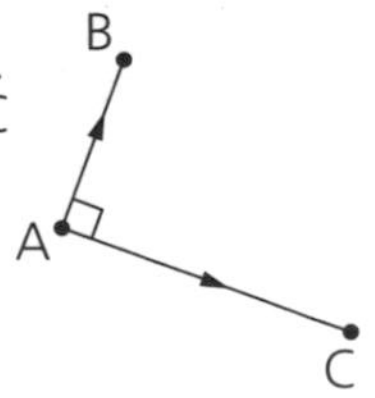

Vector 'Algebra'

Most of the 'normal' rules of algebra apply to vectors.
For instance:

$2(\boldsymbol{b} - \boldsymbol{a}) = 3(\boldsymbol{c} - \boldsymbol{a})$ rearranges to $\boldsymbol{a} = 3\boldsymbol{c} - 2\boldsymbol{b}$

$-5(\boldsymbol{v} - \boldsymbol{w}) = -5\boldsymbol{v} + 5\boldsymbol{w}$, $-(\boldsymbol{a} + \boldsymbol{b}) = -\boldsymbol{a} - \boldsymbol{b}$ etc

For any three vectors $\boldsymbol{a}$, $\boldsymbol{b}$ and $\boldsymbol{c}$ that are non-zero

$$\boldsymbol{a}.(\boldsymbol{b} + \boldsymbol{c}) = \boldsymbol{a}.\boldsymbol{b} + \boldsymbol{a}.\boldsymbol{c}$$

Also

$$\boldsymbol{a}.\boldsymbol{a} = |\,\boldsymbol{a}\,||\,\boldsymbol{a}\,| \cos 0 = |\,\boldsymbol{a}\,||\,\boldsymbol{a}\,| \times 1 = |\,\boldsymbol{a}\,|^2$$

and

$$\boldsymbol{a}.\boldsymbol{b} = \boldsymbol{b}.\boldsymbol{a}$$

Warning

$\boldsymbol{a}^2$, $(\boldsymbol{a} + \boldsymbol{b})^2$, $\sqrt{\boldsymbol{a}}$ are all meaningless.

example 12.10

All the edges of this square-based pyramid have length 3 units. Calculate $\boldsymbol{a}.(\boldsymbol{b} + \boldsymbol{c})$

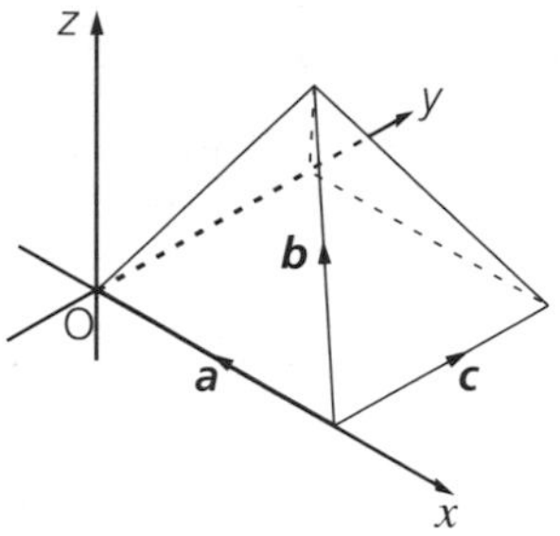

solution:

$\boldsymbol{a}.(\boldsymbol{b} + \boldsymbol{c}) = \boldsymbol{a}.\boldsymbol{b} + \boldsymbol{a}.\boldsymbol{c}$

Sloping faces are equilateral.

$= |\,\boldsymbol{a}\,||\,\boldsymbol{b}\,| \cos 60^\circ + |\,\boldsymbol{a}\,||\,\boldsymbol{c}\,| \cos 90^\circ$

The base is a square.

$= 3 \times 3 \times \frac{1}{2} + 3 \times 3 \times 0 = \boldsymbol{\frac{9}{2}}$

Basis Vectors

A **Unit Vector** has a magnitude of 1 unit.
The three unit vectors parallel to the three axes are:

$$\boldsymbol{i} = \begin{pmatrix}1\\0\\0\end{pmatrix} \quad \boldsymbol{j} = \begin{pmatrix}0\\1\\0\end{pmatrix} \quad \boldsymbol{k} = \begin{pmatrix}0\\0\\1\end{pmatrix}$$

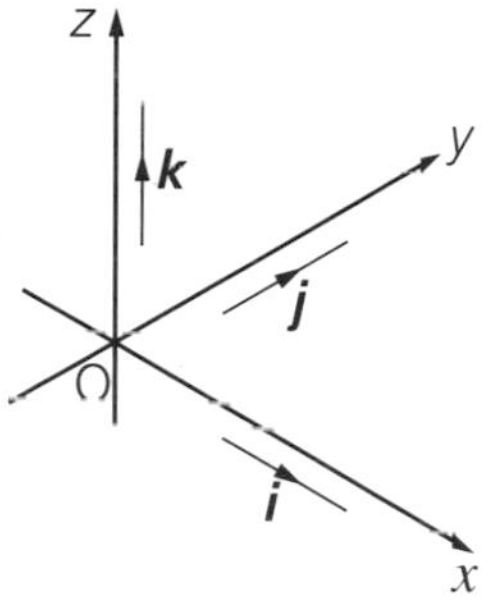

These form a set of **basis vectors** since any vector $\boldsymbol{v}$ can be written in terms of them.

If $\quad \boldsymbol{v} = \begin{pmatrix}a\\b\\c\end{pmatrix} = a\begin{pmatrix}1\\0\\0\end{pmatrix} + b\begin{pmatrix}0\\1\\0\end{pmatrix} + c\begin{pmatrix}0\\0\\1\end{pmatrix}$

then $\boldsymbol{v} = a\boldsymbol{i} + b\boldsymbol{j} + c\boldsymbol{k}$

note:
$\boldsymbol{i}.\boldsymbol{i} = \boldsymbol{j}.\boldsymbol{j} = \boldsymbol{k}.\boldsymbol{k} = 1$ and $\boldsymbol{i}.\boldsymbol{j} = \boldsymbol{j}.\boldsymbol{k} = \boldsymbol{i}.\boldsymbol{k} = 0$

example 12.11

$\boldsymbol{v} = \boldsymbol{i} - 3\boldsymbol{k}$ and $\boldsymbol{w} = 5\boldsymbol{i} - 2\boldsymbol{j} + \boldsymbol{k}$. Find a **unit** vector parallel to vector $\boldsymbol{v} - \boldsymbol{w}$.

solution:

$\boldsymbol{v} - \boldsymbol{w} = \begin{pmatrix}1\\0\\-3\end{pmatrix} - \begin{pmatrix}5\\-2\\1\end{pmatrix} = \begin{pmatrix}-4\\2\\-4\end{pmatrix}$

so $|\,\boldsymbol{v} - \boldsymbol{w}\,| = \sqrt{(-4)^2 + 2^2 + (-4)^2} = \sqrt{36} = 6$

so $\frac{1}{6}(\boldsymbol{v} - \boldsymbol{w})$ has magnitude 1 unit.

$\frac{1}{6}\begin{pmatrix}-4\\2\\-4\end{pmatrix} = \begin{pmatrix}-\frac{2}{3}\\\frac{1}{3}\\-\frac{2}{3}\end{pmatrix} = -\frac{2}{3}\boldsymbol{i} + \frac{1}{3}\boldsymbol{j} - \frac{2}{3}\boldsymbol{k}$ is the required unit vector.

Two Dimensions

All results can be adapted for two dimensions... just leave out the z-coordinate or z-component!

13. Further Differentiation and Integration

More Rules... the Trig Functions

Differentiating — The inverse process — Integrating

$f(x)$	$f'(x)$
$\sin x$	$\cos x$
$\cos x$	$-\sin x$

$f(x)$	$\int f(x)\,dx$
$\cos x$	$\sin x + C$
$\sin x$	$-\cos x + C$

note:
x is measured in **radians** or these rules break down.

example 13.1

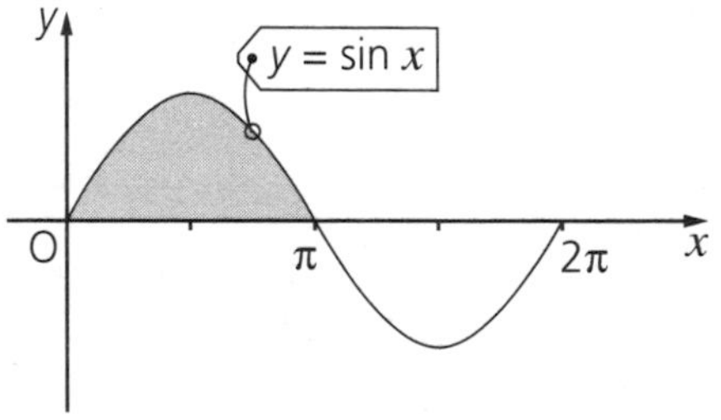

Find the shaded area.

solution:
The area is given by...

$$\int_0^{\pi} \sin x\,dx = \Big[-\cos x\Big]_0^{\pi} = -\cos \pi - (-\cos 0)$$
$$= 1 + 1 = 2$$

The shaded area = **2 unit²**.

The 'Chain Rule'

The 'chain rule' extends the scope of the normal power and trig rules.

$f(x)$	$f'(x)$
$g(h(x))$	$g'(h(x)) \times h'(x)$

Alternatively if $y = g(u)$ and $u = h(x)$

Then $\dfrac{dy}{dx} = \dfrac{dy}{du} \times \dfrac{du}{dx}$

example 13.2

Find the equation of the tangent to the graph $y = \cos x$ at the point where $x = \frac{\pi}{3}$

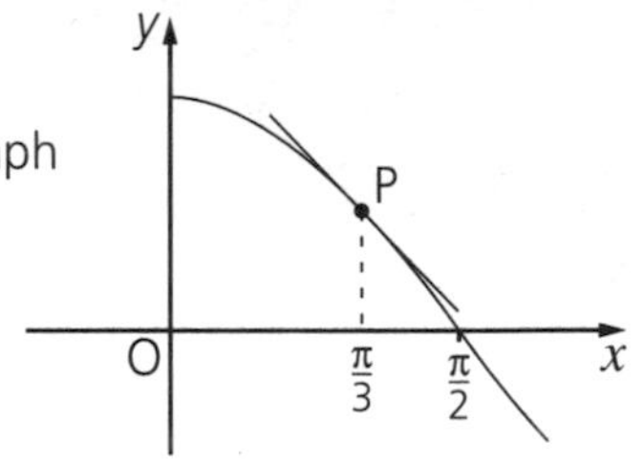

solution:

$y = \cos x$ so $\dfrac{dy}{dx} = -\sin x$

When $x = \frac{\pi}{3}$ $\dfrac{dy}{dx} = -\sin\frac{\pi}{3} = -\dfrac{\sqrt{3}}{2}$

and when $x = \frac{\pi}{3}$ $y = \cos\frac{\pi}{3} = \frac{1}{2}$

So the gradient of the tangent is $-\frac{\sqrt{3}}{2}$ and a point on the tangent is $P\left(\frac{\pi}{3}, \frac{1}{2}\right)$

The equation of the tangent is

$$y - \frac{1}{2} = -\frac{\sqrt{3}}{2}\left(x - \frac{\pi}{3}\right)$$

This gives $2y - 1 = -\sqrt{3}\left(x - \frac{\pi}{3}\right)$

or $\mathbf{2y + \sqrt{3}x = \frac{\sqrt{3}}{3}\pi + 1}$

How does this extend the 'power rule'?

Normal rule:

$y = x^n \implies \dfrac{dy}{dx} = nx^{n-1}$

Chain rule:

$y = (\text{lump})^n \implies \dfrac{dy}{dx} = n(\text{lump})^{n-1} \times \left(\text{differentiate lump}\right)$

adjustment

How does this extend the 'trig rules'?

Normal rule:

$y = \sin x \implies \dfrac{dy}{dx} = \cos x$

Chain rule:

$y = \sin(\text{lump}) \implies \dfrac{dy}{dx} = \cos(\text{lump}) \times \left(\text{differentiate lump}\right)$

adjustment

example 13.3

Differentiate ***a)*** $\sin^2 x$ ***b)*** $\cos\left(3x - \frac{\pi}{2}\right)$ ***c)*** $\sqrt{x+3}$

solution:

a) $y = (\sin x)^2 \quad \Rightarrow \frac{dy}{dx} = 2(\sin x)^1 \times \cos x$

$= 2\sin x \cos x$

$= \mathbf{\sin 2x}$ (double angle formula)

b) $y = \cos(3x - \frac{\pi}{2}) \Rightarrow \frac{dy}{dx} = -\sin(3x - \frac{\pi}{2}) \times 3$

$= \mathbf{-3\sin(3x - \frac{\pi}{2})}$

c) $y = (x+3)^{\frac{1}{2}} \quad \Rightarrow \frac{dy}{dx} = \frac{1}{2}(x+3)^{-\frac{1}{2}} \times 1$

$= \mathbf{\frac{1}{2\sqrt{x+3}}}$

Special Integrals

$$\int (ax+b)^n \, dx = \frac{(ax+b)^{n+1}}{a(n+1)} + C \quad \begin{pmatrix} n \neq -1 \\ a \neq 0 \end{pmatrix}$$

$$\int p\cos(qx+r)\, dx = \frac{p\sin(qx+r)}{q} + C \quad (q \neq 0)$$

$$\int p\sin(qx+r)\, dx = \frac{-p\cos(qx+r)}{q} + C \quad (q \neq 0)$$

This is as far as the 'chain rule' in reverse works... the 'adjustment' (q and a in the examples above) must be a **constant**.

example 13.5

Find $\int_{-1}^{1} \frac{4}{(5-3x)^2}\, dx$

solution: $\int_{-1}^{1} 4(5-3x)^{-2}\, dx = \left[\frac{4(5-3x)^{-1}}{-3\times(-1)}\right]_{-1}^{1}$

$= \left[\frac{4}{3(5-3x)}\right]_{-1}^{1} = \frac{4}{3(5-3\times 1)} - \frac{4}{3(5-3\times(-1))}$

$= \frac{4}{3\times 2} - \frac{4}{3\times 8} = \frac{4}{6} - \frac{1}{6} = \frac{3}{6} = \mathbf{\frac{1}{2}}$

example 13.4

Calculate the area enclosed by the curves $y = \sin x$ and $y = \sin 2x$ in the range $0 \leq x \leq \frac{\pi}{2}$ (shaded area in the diagram).

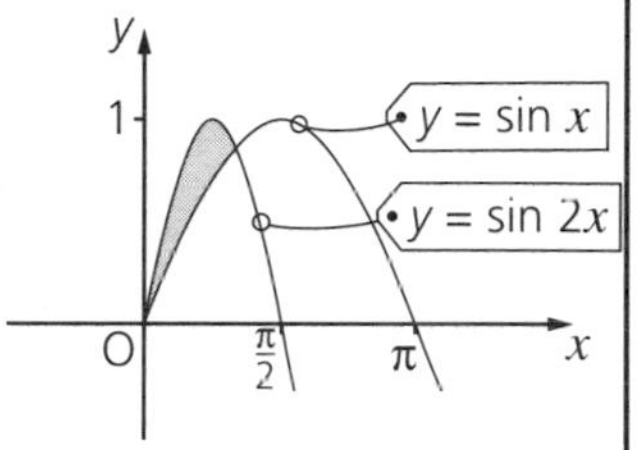

solution:

To find the points of intersection solve: $\left.\begin{array}{l} y = \sin 2x \\ y = \sin x \end{array}\right\}$

So $\sin 2x = \sin x \Rightarrow \sin 2x - \sin x = 0$

$\Rightarrow 2\sin x\cos x - \sin x = 0$

Factorising gives: $\sin x(2\cos x - 1) = 0$

$\sin x = 0$ or $\cos x = \frac{1}{2}$

$x = 0, \pi, 2\pi, \ldots \qquad x = \frac{\pi}{3}, \frac{5\pi}{3}, \ldots$

The point of intersection of interest is when $x = \frac{\pi}{3}$

Required area $= \int_0^{\frac{\pi}{3}} \sin 2x - \sin x\, dx$

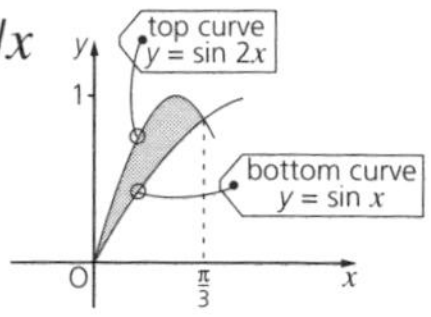

$= \left[\frac{-\cos 2x}{2} + \cos x\right]_0^{\frac{\pi}{3}}$

$= \frac{-\cos\frac{2\pi}{3}}{2} + \cos\frac{\pi}{3} - \left(\frac{-\cos 0}{2} + \cos 0\right)$

$= \frac{-(-\frac{1}{2})}{2} + \frac{1}{2} - \left(-\frac{1}{2} + 1\right)$

$= \frac{1}{4} + \frac{1}{2} + \frac{1}{2} - 1 = \mathbf{\frac{1}{4}}$ **unit²**

14. Logarithmic and Exponential Functions

Some Graphical Reminders

The exponential function (base a)

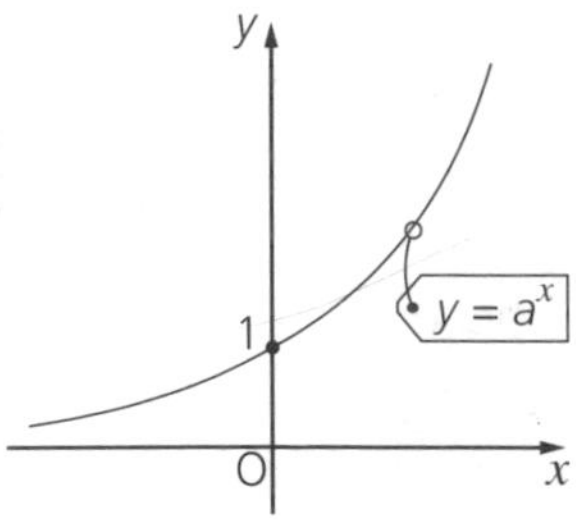

A growth curve ($a > 1$)

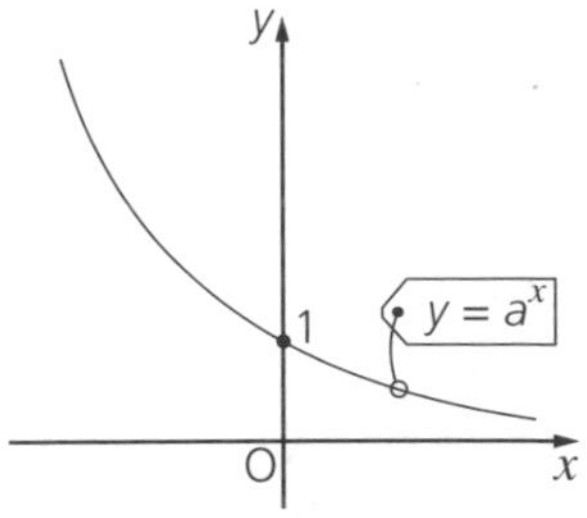

A decay curve ($0 < a < 1$)

The logarithmic function (base a)

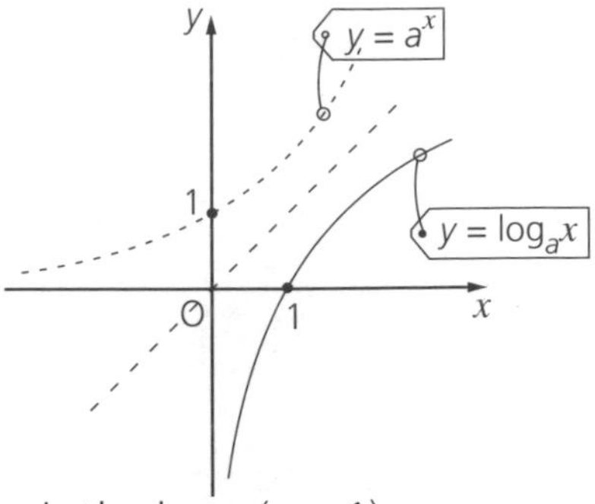

a is the base ($a > 1$)

Power Statements/Log Statements

$a^y = x \longleftrightarrow \log_a x = y$

'power statement' **'log statement'**

$\log_a x$: Useful thinking is 'what power of a gives x ?'.

For example:

$\log_5 125$: 'What power of 5 gives 125?'
$5^3 = 125$ so $\log_5 125 = 3$

The Laws of Logs

$a^m \times a^n = a^{m+n} \longleftrightarrow \log_a(xy) = \log_a x + \log_a y$

$\frac{a^m}{a^n} = a^{m-n} \longleftrightarrow \log_a\left(\frac{x}{y}\right) = \log_a x - \log_a y$

$(a^m)^n = a^{mn} \longleftrightarrow \log_a(x^n) = n\log_a x$

and some particular examples are...

$a^0 = 1 \longleftrightarrow \log_a 1 = 0$

$a^1 = a \longleftrightarrow \log_a a = 1$

The Number e

The special number e = 2·71828182... used as a base gives:

the **natural exponential function**.

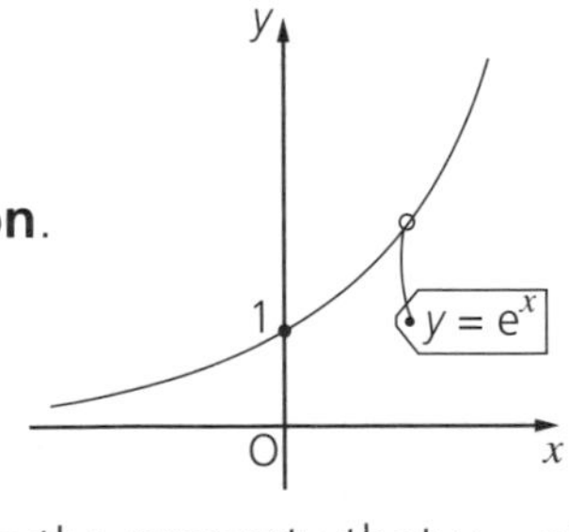

This special base e has the property that $y = e^x$ gives $\frac{dy}{dx} = e^x$. The graph $y = e^x$ is identical to its gradient graph!

This is the **natural logarithm function**.

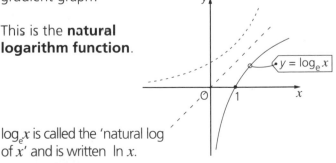

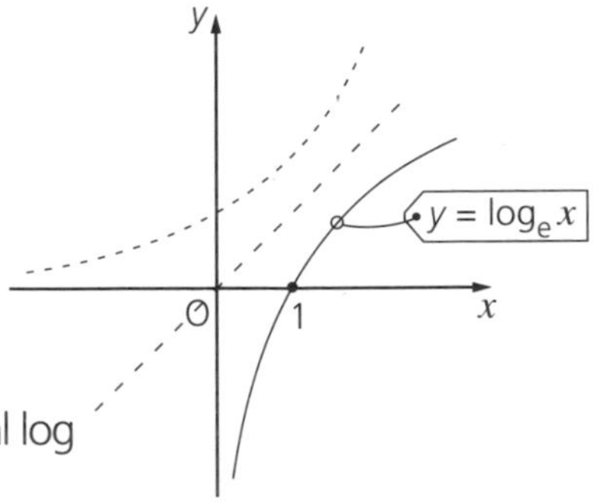

$\log_e x$ is called the 'natural log of x' and is written $\ln x$.

example 14.1

Write:
a) $3^2 = 9$ as a log statement
b) $\log_5 125 = 3$ as a power statement.

solution:
a) $3^2 = 9 \longleftrightarrow \log_3 9 = 2$
b) $\log_5 125 = 3 \longleftrightarrow 5^3 = 125$

example 14.2

Simplify: $5\log_8 2 + \log_8 4 - \log_8 16$

solution 1

$\log_8 2^5 + \log_8 4 - \log_8 16$

$= \log_8 \frac{2^5 \times 4}{16}$ (To add the logs, multiply the numbers. To subtract the logs, divide the numbers.)

$= \log_8 \frac{32 \times 4}{16} = \log_8 8 = \mathbf{1}$

solution 2

$5\log_8 2 + \log_8 2^2 - \log_8 2^4$

$= 5\log_8 2 + 2\log_8 2 - 4\log_8 2$

$= 3\log_8 2 = \log_8 2^3 = \log_8 8 = \mathbf{1}$

Using Your Calculator

(e^x) gives powers of e
(ln) gives log to the base e

These buttons 'undo' each other… e^x and $\ln x$ are inverse operations.

(10^x) gives powers of 10
(log) gives log to the base 10

These buttons 'undo' each other… 10^x and $\log_{10}x$ are inverse operations.

example 14.3

Solve:
a) $\ln x = 5$ ***b)*** $\log_{10}x = 2{\cdot}9$ ***c)*** $e^x = 4{\cdot}5$ ***d)*** $10^x = 2$

solution:
In each case rewrite the statement using
$a^y = x \longleftrightarrow \log_a x = y$

a) $\ln x = 5 \Rightarrow x = e^5 \doteqdot 148{\cdot}4$ (using (e^x))
b) $\log_{10}x = 2{\cdot}9 \Rightarrow x = 10^{2{\cdot}9} \doteqdot 794{\cdot}3$ (using (10^x))
c) $e^x = 4{\cdot}5 \Rightarrow x = \ln 4{\cdot}5 \doteqdot 1{\cdot}50$ (using (ln))
d) $10^x = 2 \Rightarrow x = \log_{10}2 \doteqdot 0{\cdot}301$ (using (log))

example 14.4

Solve $5^x = 4$

solution:
Take logs of both sides (either base e **or** base 10)
so $\log_{10}(5^x) = \log_{10}4$
$\Rightarrow x\log_{10}5 = \log_{10}4$
$\Rightarrow x = \dfrac{\log_{10}4}{\log_{10}5} \doteqdot 0{\cdot}861$

example 14.5

Evaluate $\log_3 2$
Let $x = \log_3 2$
Then $3^x = 2$
Now take logs of both sides (base e or 10)
So $\log_e 3^x = \log_e 2 \Rightarrow x\ln 3 = \ln 2$

$\Rightarrow x = \dfrac{\ln 2}{\ln 3} \doteqdot 0{\cdot}631 \left(\text{check } \dfrac{\log_{10}2}{\log_{10}3} \text{ gives the same}\right)$

example 14.6

The diagram shows the graph $y = a\log_2(x + b)$
Find the values of a and b.

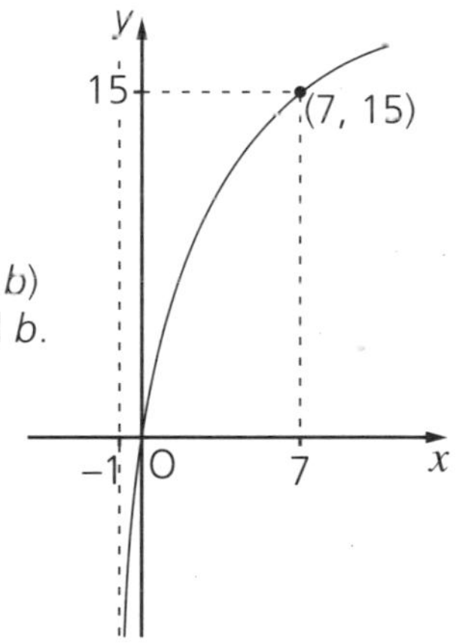

solution:
The 'normal' log graph has been shifted by 1 unit to the left.

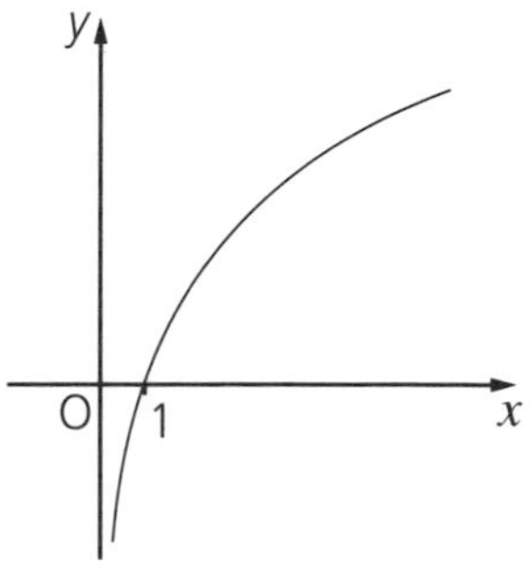

So $\boldsymbol{b = 1}$ (see example 3.6 on page 13)
giving $y = a\log_2(x + 1)$

Since (7,15) lies on the graph, $x = 7$ and $y = 15$ must satisfy the equation.
So $15 = a\log_2(7 + 1) = a\log_2 8 = a \times 3$ ($2^3 = 8$)
so $\boldsymbol{a = 5}$ giving $y = 5\log_2(x + 1)$

example 14.7

If £I are invested at r% interest (compounded annually), then the value £V, of the investment after n years is given by $V = \left(1+\dfrac{r}{100}\right)^n I$
At 8% p.a. how long would £100 take to double in value?

solution:

$$\frac{V}{I} = \left(1+\frac{r}{100}\right)^n \Rightarrow \log\frac{V}{I} = n\log\left(1+\frac{r}{100}\right)$$

$$\Rightarrow n = \frac{\log\frac{V}{I}}{\log\left(1+\frac{r}{100}\right)}$$

When $I = 100$, $V = 200$ and $r = 8$ then

$$n = \frac{\log\frac{200}{100}}{\log(1+\frac{8}{100})} = \frac{\log 2}{\log 1{\cdot}08}$$

$= 9{\cdot}006\ldots$ ie **9 years**.

Straight Line Graphs

$y = ax^b$

Taking the log of both sides gives:

$$\log y = \log(ax^b) = \log a + \log x^b$$

so $\quad \log y = b \log x + \log a$

compare $\quad Y = m X + c$

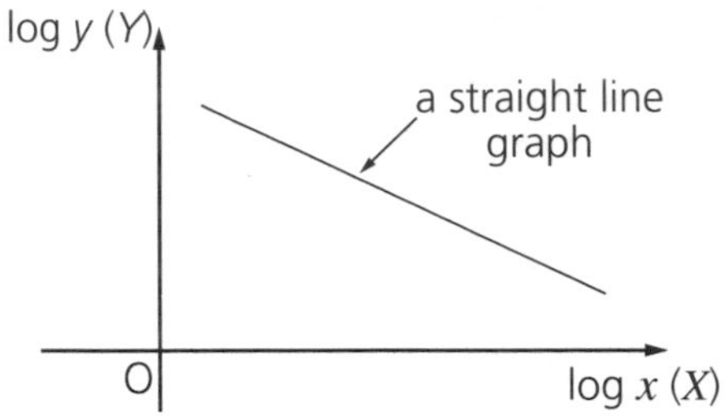

If plotting the values of log y against the values of log x results in a straight line graph then this confirms a relationship of the form

$$y = ax^b$$

for suitable values of constants a and b.

$y = ab^x$

Taking the log of both sides gives:

$$\log y = \log(ab^x) = \log a + \log b^x$$

so $\quad \log y = (\log b)\, x + \log a$

compare $\quad Y = m x + c$

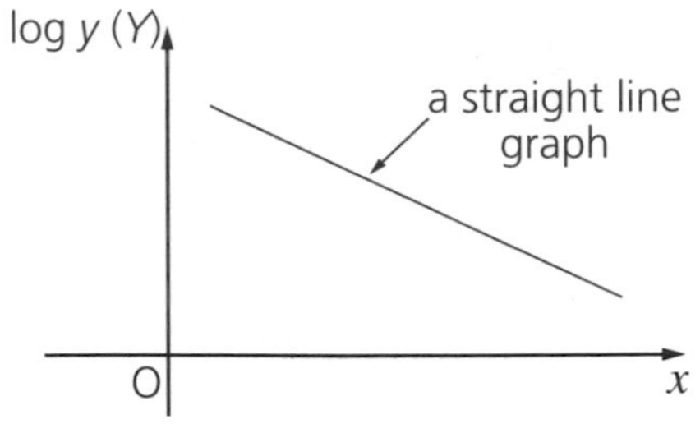

If plotting the values of log y against the values of x results in a straight line graph then this confirms a relationship of the form

$$y = ab^x$$

for suitable values of constants a and b.

example 14.8

It is suspected that the relationship between x and y is of the form

$$y = ax^b$$

and the graph confirms this.
Find the values of constants a and b.

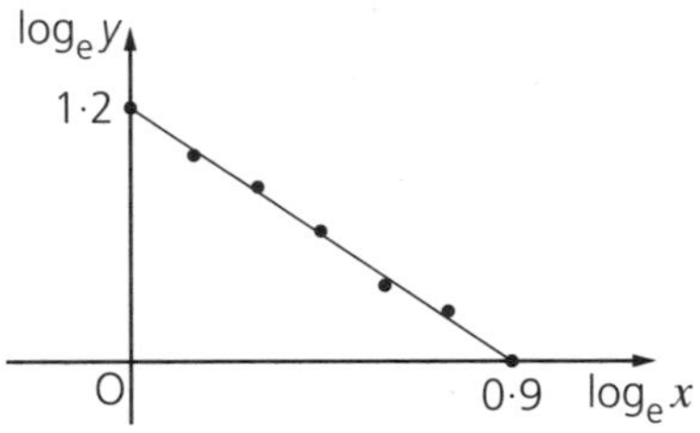

solution:

$y = ax^b$ gives $\log_e y = \log_e(ax^b) = \log_e a + \log_e x^b$

so $\quad \log_e y = b \log_e x + \log_e a$

compare $\quad Y = m X + c$

For the given graph, the gradient (m) gives b.
Use A(0, 1·2) and B(0·9, 0)

so $m_{AB} = \dfrac{1 \cdot 2 - 0}{0 - 0 \cdot 9} = \dfrac{1 \cdot 2}{-0 \cdot 9} = -\dfrac{12}{9} = -\dfrac{4}{3}$ so $b = -\dfrac{4}{3}$

The y-intercept (0, c) gives $\log_e a$ ($c = \log_e a$).
The intercept is (0, 1·2)
so $\log_e a = 1 \cdot 2 \Rightarrow a = e^{1 \cdot 2} \doteqdot 3 \cdot 32$ (using e^x button)

This gives the relationship $\boldsymbol{y = 3 \cdot 32\, x^{-\frac{4}{3}}}$

Linear Combinations of Sine and Cosine

Look at these graphs...

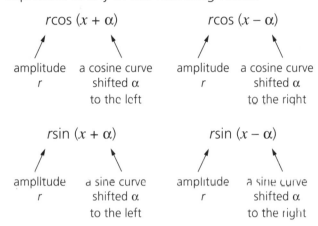

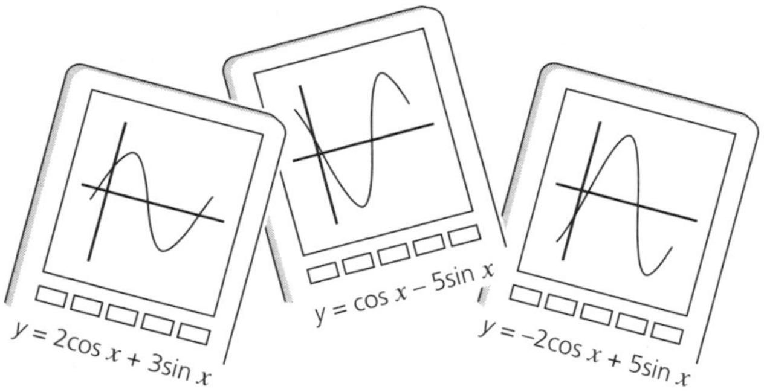

Graphs with equations of the form

$$y = a\cos x + b\sin x$$

where a and b are constants, are always sine or cosine graphs with differing amplitudes and shifted left or right. They can therefore be expressed in any of the following forms:

$r\cos(x + \alpha)$ — amplitude r; a cosine curve shifted α to the left

$r\cos(x - \alpha)$ — amplitude r; a cosine curve shifted α to the right

$r\sin(x + \alpha)$ — amplitude r; a sine curve shifted α to the left

$r\sin(x - \alpha)$ — amplitude r; a sine curve shifted α to the right

note: Only use r positive ($r > 0$).

Finding r and α

To write $a\cos x + b\sin x$ as a sine or cosine curve...

step 1 Choose one of $r\cos(x + \alpha)$, $r\cos(x - \alpha)$, $r\sin(x + \alpha)$, $r\sin(x - \alpha)$.

step 2 Expand your chosen expression using the appropriate addition formula.

step 3 Compare coefficients of $\cos x$... they are equal. Compare coefficients of $\sin x$... they are equal.

step 4 Solve the pair of resulting equations to find r and α:

1) Divide the left sides and the right sides of the equations to get a value for $\frac{\sin\alpha}{\cos\alpha} = \tan\alpha$. Determine the correct quadrant.

2) Square the sides and add. Then use $\sin^2\alpha + \cos^2\alpha = 1$ to find r^2 and then r ($r > 0$).

example 15.1

Express $2\cos x° + 3\sin x°$ in the form $r\cos(x - \alpha)°$ where $r > 0$.

solution:

Expand $r\cos(x - \alpha)°$ giving

$$r\cos x°\cos\alpha° + r\sin x°\sin\alpha°$$

Compare $\quad 2\cos x° + 3\sin x°$

So $r\cos\alpha° = 2$, $r\sin\alpha° = 3$ — $\sin\alpha°$, $\cos\alpha°$ are both positive thus $\alpha°$ is in the first quadrant.

Use $\frac{\sin\alpha°}{\cos\alpha°}$:

$$\frac{r\sin\alpha°}{r\cos\alpha°} = \frac{3}{2}$$

$$\tan\alpha° = \frac{3}{2}$$

so $\alpha° \doteqdot 56{\cdot}3°$
(first quadrant only)

Use $\sin^2\alpha° + \cos^2\alpha° = 1$:

$$r^2\cos^2\alpha° + r^2\sin^2\alpha° = 2^2 + 3^2$$
$$r^2(\cos^2\alpha° + \sin^2\alpha°) = 4 + 9$$
$$r^2 \times 1 = 13$$

so $r = \sqrt{13}$ ($r > 0$)

So $2\cos x° + 3\sin x° = \mathbf{\sqrt{13}\cos(x - 56{\cdot}3)°}$

example 15.2

Express $\cos x - \sqrt{3}\sin x$ in the form $r\sin(x + \alpha)$ where $0 < \alpha < 2\pi$ and $r > 0$

solution:

$r\sin(x + \alpha) = r\sin x\cos\alpha + r\cos x\sin\alpha$

Compare $\quad 1\cos x - \sqrt{3}\sin x$

This gives

$r\cos\alpha = -\sqrt{3}$
$r\sin\alpha = 1$

In this case $\sin\alpha$ is positive and $\cos\alpha$ is negative so α is in the second quadrant.

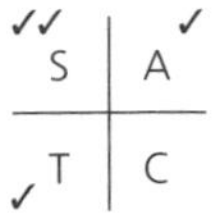

$$\frac{r\sin\alpha}{r\cos\alpha} = \frac{1}{-\sqrt{3}}$$

$$\tan\alpha = -\frac{1}{\sqrt{3}}$$

(2nd quadrant)

So $\quad \alpha = \pi - \frac{\pi}{6}$

$$\alpha = \frac{5\pi}{6}$$

$$r^2\sin^2\alpha + r^2\cos^2\alpha = 1^2 + (-\sqrt{3})^2 = 4$$

$$r^2(\sin^2\alpha + \cos^2\alpha) = r^2 \times 1 = r^2 = 4$$

So $\quad r = 2\ (r > 0)$

Giving $\mathbf{\cos x - \sqrt{3}\sin x = 2\sin\left(x + \frac{5\pi}{6}\right)}$

Solving Equations

To solve $a\cos x + b\sin x = c$

step 1 Express the left side in one of the forms...
$r\cos(x \pm \alpha)$ or $r\sin(x \pm \alpha)$

step 2 Divide through by r to give

$$\cos(x \pm \alpha) = \frac{c}{r} \text{ or } \sin(x \pm \alpha) = \frac{c}{r}$$

and solve in the 'usual' way.

example 15.3

Find algebraically the values of x between 0 and 180 for which $12\sin x° - 5\cos x° = 10$.

solution:

Expressing $12\sin x° - 5\cos x°$ in the form $r\sin(x - \alpha)°$ gives $13\sin(x - 22{\cdot}6)°$

The equation becomes

$$13\sin(x - 22{\cdot}6)° = 10$$

so $\quad \sin(x - 22{\cdot}6)° = \frac{10}{13}$

($(x - 22{\cdot}6)°$ is in 1st or 2nd quadrants)
(1st quadrant angle is $50{\cdot}3°$)

so $x° - 22{\cdot}6° = 50{\cdot}3°$ or $180° - 50{\cdot}3° = 129{\cdot}7°$
giving $x° = 50{\cdot}3° + 22{\cdot}6°$ or $129{\cdot}7° + 22{\cdot}6°$
so $x° = \mathbf{72{\cdot}9}°$ or $\mathbf{152{\cdot}3}°$

Check on graphic calculator.

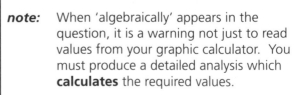

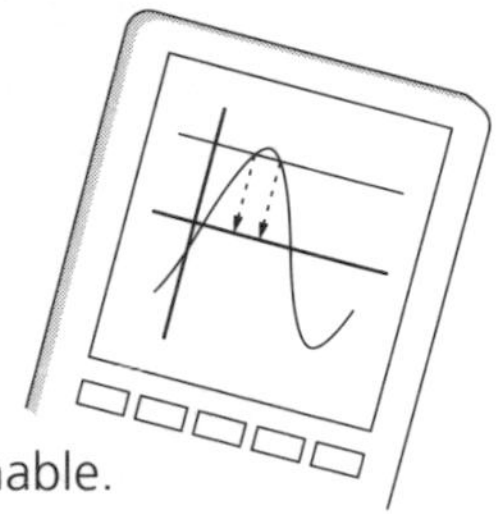

The graphs $y = 13\sin(x - 22{\cdot}6)°$ **and** $y = 10$ are shown.
The answers appear reasonable.

note: When 'algebraically' appears in the question, it is a warning not just to read values from your graphic calculator. You must produce a detailed analysis which **calculates** the required values.

Maximum and Minimum Values

To determine the Maximum/Minimum value of $a\cos x + b\sin x$ and to find the corresponding values of x:

step 1 Write $a\cos x + b\sin x$ in one of the forms $r\cos(x \pm \alpha)$ or $r\sin(x \pm \alpha)$.

step 2 The maximum value is r.
The minimum value is $-r$.

step 3 Set the angles $x + \alpha$ or $x - \alpha$ equal to the 'normal' angle for which sin/cos is at a max/min (see the diagrams for examples) and then solve to find x.

A sine curve $y = r\sin(x - \alpha)$

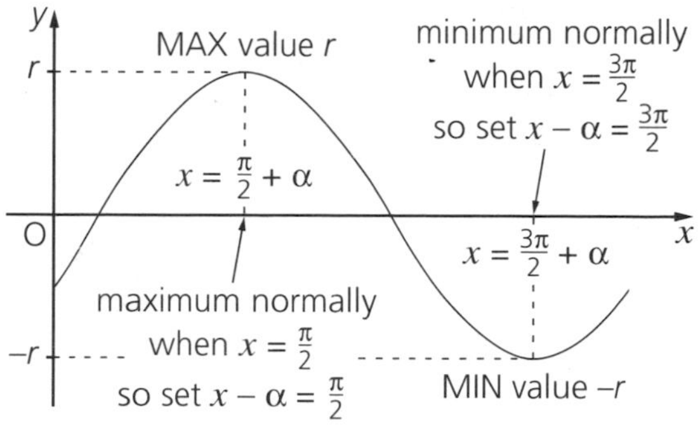

A cosine curve $y = r\cos(x - \alpha)$

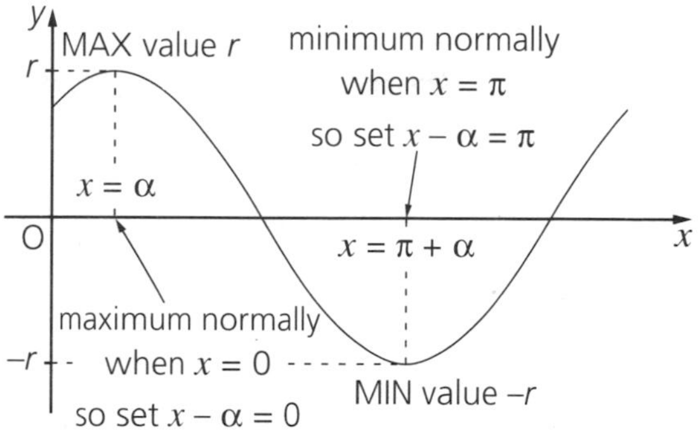

example 15.4

Find the maximum value of L where
$L = \cos 2\theta + \sqrt{3}\sin 2\theta$ and the corresponding values for θ where $0 \le \theta \le 2\pi$.

solution:

$\cos 2\theta + \sqrt{3}\sin 2\theta$ can be expressed as $r\cos(2\theta - \alpha)$

giving $r = 2$ and $\alpha = \frac{\pi}{3}$ so $L = 2\cos\left(2\theta - \frac{\pi}{3}\right)$

The maximum value of L is **2** and this happens

when $2\theta - \frac{\pi}{3} = 0, 2\pi, \ldots$

$\Rightarrow \quad 2\theta = \frac{\pi}{3}, 2\pi + \frac{\pi}{3}, \ldots$

$\Rightarrow \quad 2\theta = \frac{\pi}{3}, \frac{7\pi}{3}, \ldots$

$\Rightarrow \quad \theta = \frac{\pi}{6}, \frac{7\pi}{6}, \ldots$

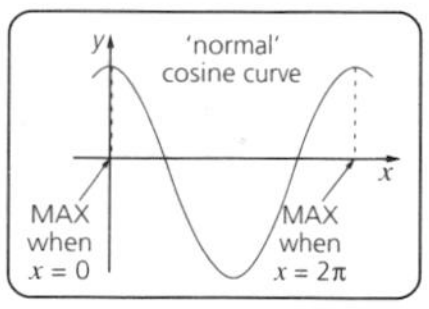

So $\boldsymbol{\theta = \frac{\pi}{6}}$ **and** $\boldsymbol{\theta = \frac{7\pi}{6}}$ are the required values
(all other values are outside the range $0 \le \theta \le 2\pi$).

Index